D0438607

PUBLIC EYE

Also by Brian Fawcett

MY CAREER WITH THE LEAFS AND
OTHER STORIES

CAPITAL TALES

THE SECRET JOURNAL OF
ALEXANDER MACKENZIE

CAMBODIA: A BOOK FOR
PEOPLE WHO FIND TELEVISION
TOO SLOW

PUBLIC EYE

AN INVESTIGATION INTO
THE DISAPPEARANCE OF
THE WORLD

Brian
Fawcett

GROVE WEIDENFELD
NEW YORK

Published by Grove Weidenfeld
A division of Wheatland Corporation
841 Broadway
New York, NY 10003-4793

Letter from Rainer Maria Rilke reprinted from Letters of Rainer Maria Rilke,
1910-1926, translated by Jane Bannard Greene and M. D. Herter Norton,
by permission of W. W. Norton & Company, Inc. Copyright 1947, 1948 by
W. W. Norton and Company, Inc. Copyright renewed 1972 by M. D. Norton.

Library of Congress Cataloging-in-Publication Data

Fawcett, Brian, 1944–
    Public eye : an investigation into the disappearance of the world /
    Brian Fawcett. — 1st ed.
        p.   cm.
    ISBN 0-8021-1142-4 (alk. paper)
    I. Title.
PR9199.3.F39P8   1990
813'.54—dc20   89-25671
                                                             CIP

Manufactured in the United States of America

Printed on acid-free paper

Designed by Irving Perkins Associates

First Edition 1990

10   9   8   7   6   5   4   3   2   1

ACKNOWLEDGMENTS

This book has research and editorial collaborators: Nancy Boyd, Robin Ridington, Christopher Dewdney, Barbara Howell, Lee Trentadue, Stephen Duguid, Peter Lynch, T. R. Elton, Phil Shaddock, Joost Bakker, Erling Christensen, Bill Schermbrucker, and Robin Blaser.

I would also like to thank the Four Wings and the Blue Parrot cafés for providing perspective and office space.

Early versions of several episodes have been bravely published by *The Capilano Review* and the *Journal of Wild Culture*.

The inscription is taken from *Letters of Rainer Maria Rilke, 1910–1926*, translated by Jane B. Greene and M. D. Herter, Norton (New York: 1947), pp. 374–75.

Like the evening television news, this is a work of fiction. All resemblances to real persons and things, living or dead, is purely intentional—unless they find it objectionable, of course. . . .

CONTENTS

CONTENTS

vi

. . . we must introduce what is *here* seen and touched into the wider, into the widest orbit. Not into a beyond whose shadow darkens the earth, but into a whole, into *the whole*. . . . Now, empty indifferent things are pouring across, sham things, *dummy life*. . . . Live things, things lived and conscient of us, are running out and can no longer be replaced. *We are perhaps the last still to have known such things. On us rests the responsibility not alone of preserving* their *memory (that would be little and unreliable), but their human and laral value*. . . . We are . . . these transformers of the earth; our entire existence, the flights and plunges of our love, everything qualifies us for this task (*besides which there exists, essentially, no other*).

Rainer Maria Rilke
(letter to Witold von Hulewicz,
postmarked November 13, 1925)

PUBLIC NOTICE

This book is an attempt to track a fundamental and monstrous change in the human condition and in human consciousness. The world is disappearing around us, and you and I are disappearing with it.

The Dominican monastic order has a procedure by which no idea can be discussed without first agreeing on the definitions of the terms to be used during the discussion. There are two very wobbly terms in my opening statement. *World* is one; *disappearing* is the other.

Most simply stated, the world is the sum total of human acts, aspirations, imaginations, neuroses, and psychoses. It is what we make and believe and dither over; the realm of our artifice, distinct from "nature," "earth," and from "cosmology." Over the last century, the human species has made astonishing leaps in its three-thousand-year struggle to separate itself from the limitations of nature. These leaps have been fueled mostly by technological innovation, but they've also been mandatory. Advances in population over the last century have taken our numbers to levels beyond what any "natural" system could support. In 1945 we entered a new phase, when we created the means to destroy nature itself. We can now put an end to ourselves and to all life on the planet in less than an hour, an accomplishment that is, if nothing else, a signal that we must be the masters of our collective fate and the caretakers of the planet.

That we have not responded to that signal is an extremely urgent matter, but for the purposes of our definitions, it is secondary to the fact that we now live in a *world* that is mostly of our own devising and disposal. It is the *world,* not nature, that is the primary ground of consciousness. In the past several decades

ix

a world economy has emerged. Now we are faced with the possibility—or the reality—of a world culture. Most often that world economy and culture are yoked together in Utopian terms as the Global Village. We're becoming a single tribe in a single world enclave—whether we like it or not.

The implications of *disappearing* lie hidden within the structure of the word itself. A person or thing that disappears does not necessarily die or cease to exist. He, she, or it rather ceases to appear, with the etymological implication that appearance has been displaced or suppressed—removed to a half-life of invisibility: the classical realm of Dis, the god of the underworld.

South American dictatorships, for instance, have perfected the practice of picking up political dissidents and "disappearing" them. Sometimes the victims are shot and buried in clandestine graves or thrown from helicopters at high altitudes over the ocean or jungle. Other victims cease to appear for periods of weeks or months, but then their mangled bodies will sometimes reappear in garbage dumps or street corners or even on their own doorsteps. A few victims, however, are released alive, sometimes after being brutally tortured, but occasionally without injury. To disappear is not to die. It is a cessation of appearance.

Political "disappearances" are therefore different from an execution or an imprisonment. The difference lies in the effect the disappearance has on the community of those who have not been disappeared. The disappeared have been sent to the realm of Dis—of nonexistence. But because there is the chance that they are not dead but only absent temporarily, the undisappeared too are plunged into a terrorized limbo, not knowing if their loved one is alive or dead, and fearful of any significant act that might occasion their death. As a means of sapping political will and suppressing dissent, no more effective weapon has ever been devised.

I use the term, then, with three connected meanings. *To be disappeared* is to have the right of political (or social or cultural) expression taken away. *To disappear* is to cease to be visible and distinct to oneself and others, along with its original meaning of "to vanish," or "to not appear." A third usage is the transitive application, in which one would disappear another person or thing by lethal violence or imprisonment, or, by undermining its psychic and physical autonomy to the point where it is unable to recognize itself or be recognized by its community.

With some exceptions, it is this last effect that is the truest subject of this book's investigation. I am looking for the kind, extent, and cause of the disappearance of the world. But I am also trying to locate and define the agency—or agencies—that cause the phenomenon, and I am looking for antidotes.

A few technical warnings are in order. This book is not the record of a conventional detective investigation. "Public eye" implies an attempt to see *everything* that is—or ought to be—public, or at least to uncover the *matrix* of everything public.

Common sense says that isn't possible. *Everything* can't be seen and treated, and an attempted investigation of it would require the combined resources of the human species. In short, I'm crazy and this project is a logical and practical absurdity. But since the alternatives this culture offers me as an imaginative writer constitute a diminution and a falsification of human reality, I've felt compelled to conduct the investigation anyway. What follows, therefore, is also an attempt to corrupt the technical boundaries of contemporary literary convention.

I've proceeded by a number of routes and methods. Some of them might seem suspiciously like postmodernist caprice, wherein history, its technologies, and its ideas are rearranged into and subordinated to spurious objectifications of private perceptual and cultural parameters that valorize idiosyncrasy at the expense of intelligibility. The intent of the methods I use isn't meant to be a dance before the bonfires of that high-chic barbarism. Pretty well anyone with a full deck, some healthy curiosity, and an uneasiness about the conditions of things will find the investigation easy to follow.

To make it more explicit, a few things about the way the investigation operates require elaboration. First of all, the book looks, well, odd. It has parallel texts, with different narrators. The upper text mostly examines the world through fictional narrators. The chief one I've called Public Eye. This part of the text dramatizes the disappearances, the disappeared, and presents some alternatives and remedies.

The lower text, or subtext, discusses the implications of the various upper-text episodes, revealing openly that there is an author behind everything, and that this author is pursuing a discursive mission instead of pretending indifference or abandoning the reader to the intellectual chaos of undefined and fantastical subtexts we're supposed to hold in common. I don't want imaginative fiction to be orphaned from discourse any longer. In the world, they are lonely for the company of the other, and each is dangerous without the other. Without them in proximity, I'm convinced the atomization of human community and conciousness will continue.

I also want to ensure that my readers are reminded that an entirely fallible authority is working behind the scenes, and to guard against the now-lethal willful suspension of disbelief. I want the reader's critical eyes and ears at the forefront, and then for a slightly irregular purpose. The episodes presented are meant to be more than artificially coherent kicks at contrived cans. The craziest and most frightening things you'll find in this book are the ones drawn most directly from ordinary life. I learned long ago that the ability to invent things is the least important skill for a fiction writer. The real trick, particularly in our own era, is that of tilting the sets enough that readers can perceive how crazy the world has become. Anyone who proposes that the truth is straightforward and can be presented in an orderly linear way should make us deeply suspicious.

For all its apparent complexity, the text ought to be user-friendly, at least if the reader is willing to forgo the fantastical coherence of origin, tone, and decision that fiction readers are accustomed to. I've aimed at achieving general complexity, but with a multiplicity of entrances and/or handholds that allow entry at almost any point. I've tried to create a text that accurately

opens itself to the best side of contemporary cognitive habitation, with its enhanced ability (and hunger) for contextualizing. Try reading the top text until you become irritable or confused or bored, then move to the subtext and do the same. When and if that starts to slip, go back to the top. About the only reading strategy that doesn't seem to work is the conventional one of trying to hold on to the old fetish of reading from the top to bottom of each page.

Since I'm not an idealist and my delusions of grandeur are intermittent, I'd gladly settle for a sort of never-completed story that will eventually devour literary formalism as we've come to know it. The formal ideal, of course, would be to create a neural and cultural data base whose dynamic will force a rejection of the authority of the author and selfish authority in general.

My philosophical aim is even more modest. If this book addresses fundamental questions, however provisionally and tentative the address is, and if it causes readers to do the same, then I will be more than satisfied.

You, as my reader, should feel free to intervene with information and insights of your own. Outbursts of laughter are also welcome. If you feel strongly enough about it, send them to me personally. Even a "heh, heh" or an "Oh God, no" on a postcard will do. There is no reason to halt a discourse on important issues simply because a text is published in book form. If I'm right about any of what I've just written, it won't be possible.

Having given you my general plan, I should try to be more specific about what is being investigated. It concerns a series of disappearances. These disappearances are related, ongoing—in progress—and highly problematical.

Proving that someone or something is *in the process of disappearing* is an evidential absurdity, particularly if the mode of disappearance isn't directly violent and dramatic. Mind and body parts that are simply fading or shriveling propose disease, not crime. To make it worse, the instinctive response is avoidance, not outrage or curiosity. Who wants to risk infection?

The social and physical environments in which you and I can be conscious of one another as responsible individuals acting in responsible communities are dissolving before our eyes, being sequestered, painted over, asphalted. We are being drawn into a doomsday nexus in which, for a few more decades, we will consume the material resources of this planet with astonishing rapidity. While we do that, we will also exhaust and even destroy the intellectual resources with which to respond to the crisis we're creating.

Subliminal or clandestine design is a new kind of intellectual terrorism our entire civilization appears to be falling back from, defeated, at every nexus of its culture and subcultures. That terrorism, and its sources, is the villain of this book. I've given that villain a name, and have tried to describe some of its faces. You may have different names for it. For sure, all of us have glimpsed it, and many of us find ourselves beneath its cold stare every day of our lives. Whether I get this right or not, the disappearance of the world is now the tale of the tribe, and our survival probably depends on how intelligently we can render an account of the dangers that await us in the retribalization that is taking place, invisibly, in our midst.

This book, its primary narrator, and its subtext will chiefly be askers of questions. The investigation deliberately inhabits the shadowy realm of probability, with frequent forays into the para-noically speculative. But along the way, my primary narrator and I have tried to ask some questions about authority and the admin-istration of social justice our generation of North American writers has by and large ceased to address.

What *would* we do if we had the power to change the things that are wrong? Most writers want nothing to do with such a question. My response is to propose that in the realm of imagina-tion, it is a poor show to walk away from it. What will become of us if we can imagine no other world than the one we appear to be in?

These days writers are permitted and occasionally encouraged to criticize. But no government and few citizens would think of asking us to make practical suggestions, and never to propose fundamental changes. Such matters should be left to the experts, or to the people elected to make changes. Hurrumppphhh. Professional privilege.

I don't have any faith in the powers of professionalism, I don't respect professional privileges, and I don't offer professional courtesies unless someone has a gun at my head. And neither does my narrator.

Maybe we *must* rethink authority and its current stupidities, corruptions, and evils. But how? My instinct is to devise a new— or long-absent—variety of authority that is humane, educative, and—here's a welcome change—intentionally funny.

Sure it's a fantasy maybe it's the ultimate one. But the world is built from *someone's* fantasies, and the ones that govern our lives are a lot sicker than anything you'll find in these pages. Consider the nightmare logic in which our contemporary military and diplomatic systems are rooted: mutual assured destruction, 20,000 nuclear warheads, double subsidized wheat rotting in grain elevators while millions starve to death, and a thousand other insanities and injustices.

Interspersed among the Public Eye episodes, you'll find some provisional antidotes to the visible authorities we face. Let me give you a preview:

For me, one of the daily annoyances is that the only occasions for general social action we have seem to occur when we're trying to control uncooperative social groups or subjugate or kill people from other countries. There are any number of odious but necessary social tasks under our noses, ones that should be shared by the whole society instead of handed over to specialist groups who are immediately and permanently corrupted or crippled by doing them. The social and/or technological perspectives involved are a burden that should be shouldered by all of us. More important, the narrow-focus authority this kind of work generates is a threat to collective and individual sanity.

None of these tasks are aggressively military in nature. They do involve social services and require organization and attention to economies of scale. Their common characteristic is that they're ugly, and they make the people who do them ugly. Accordingly, the first antidote I'd concoct would be to create a Public Ugly Service Corps, or PUS, as follows:

The armed forces would be radically cut back in budget and numbers, and a universal draft instituted which would require from all citizens—able-bodied or otherwise—initial three-month service and two weeks' annual requalifying furloughs. Citizens would be allowed to choose between duty work as prison guards, garbage collectors, print and media editorial writers, judges, urban planners and public art gallery curators, tow-truck drivers and traffic cops. (This list is not inclusive, obviously. Feel free to add occupations.)

Imagine how it would clean up the acts of well-known public figures—or your personal friends and enemies. Think about Dan Quayle doing a stint on the garbage trucks with Noam Chomsky or Mary Hart. Michael Jackson as a prison guard, Margaret Thatcher driving a tow truck. Get the general idea?

You'll find a number of these antidotes scattered throughout the book. I'd be the first to admit that the problems they'd evoke would be as difficult to solve as the ones we already face. I'm also aware they'd require a divine right monarch to put them in place. But they're not meant to be a blueprint for Utopia. They're only there to invite you to think about practical solutions, instead of authoritative answers. And sometimes they're present strictly to make you laugh.

PUBLIC EYE

A SHORT HISTORY
OF ZIP THE PINHEAD

Don't be misled by those garish Zip the Pinhead T-shirts you see in the windows of novelty shops market-targeted at self-destructive adolescents. And don't be taken in by the Zip cartoon bookettes, the ones that allow you to feel superior to your doomed fellow-consumers without having to read about why you're all doomed. *That* version of Zip is residue from the 1960s, when normality became so unattractive that anyone in his or her right mind was either freaking out or looking for something to make him or her freak. The Zip-generated slogans of those days are still around—"Mutate Now—Avoid the Post-Bomb Rush"—but they're no longer funny.

Ask yourself the right questions. Why did social normality become a bad joke? Why, today, is public reality a surrealist's nightmare? Who—not what—was Zip the Pinhead?

The first two of those questions are each worth volumes, but I can offer quick help with the third question. Zip the Pinhead wasn't a 1960s invention constructed to satirize the optimum reality-set produced by psychotropic drugs, Walt Disney, Richard Nixon, and consumerism. His real name was William Henry Jackson, and he lived more than eighty years on this planet, making his living from 1859 through to his death in 1926 as a professional circus freak. He was entirely, bodily real. A *person,* like you and me.

Sure, he was a microcephalic, and his DNA chains were twisted a little. No shame in that. One string just happened to be imperfectly connected to another so that he came out of the starting gate with a hat size that would never be larger than $4^7/8$ and, some say, an intelligence to match it. Just for a few moments, let's forget that the words *idiot* and *stupid* exist. We are dealing with a human being here, one with a tenacious hold on life and a particular sense of reality that it might be educative to imagine—and to enact—as a critique of our own.

It is a low-ceilinged building Zip looks out across. It is warm and dark here, and the air is filled with moist, pungently organic odors that carry faint traces of ammonia. And there are sounds, comfortingly simple sounds, not quite music but rather the harmonies of bodily production. Zip tugs idly at the tuft of hair at the crown of his head, runs his fingers through the stubble surrounding it, and grunts with pleasure.

Zip is at home, encastled. It is morning, mid-November 1925, shortly after the circus season ends, Zip's working season. He's been home for a week, and already he's forgotten the curiously painful elation of being gazed at by strangers, of being jostled and pinched and shouted at, and of gazing and shouting back. What he recalls of the past season is already suffused into purer data: the brightness of the lights, the vividness of the colors, the comforts of people who seem to know him, the people who work for him and do his bidding.

Zip is the freak emeritus of John Ringling's Ringling Bros. Barnum & Bailey Circus. Zip is a relic of long-dead P. T. Barnum's collection of genetic anomalies, half-truths, outright mistakes, and sometimes, bald-assed fakes. Barnum pried Brooklyn-born Zip away from a New Jersey chicken farm and his poverty-stricken black parents when the boy was in his early teens, and Zip has been a star performer ever since, the *What-Is-It?* of the circuses' freak entourage.

Others in the entourage are more spectacular, as freaks go. Zip is touted in the billings as an African curiosity captured in Gambia by an expedition in search of giant gorillas. No mention of Brooklyn there, but Zip doesn't care where people think he came from. For him it is enough that he is there.

While Zip is working, his head is shaved, with a small braided topknot left to accentuate the conical brevity of his cranium, and he wears a furry brown jumpsuit over his diminutive frame to further accentuate his atavistic persona. On special occasions he wears a laquered oval medallion depicting George Washington, who Zip believes is, alternately or at the same time, God or P. T. Barnum.

Zip has remained a crowd favorite for more than six decades, outlasting the ever-changing Smallest Man in the World, the Bearded Ladies and Fat Women, the endless and forgettable Giants, JoJo the Dog-faced Boy, the fabulous double-wombed Myrtle Corbin with the extra pair of legs poking from under her dress—and the promise of a sexuality more exotic than anything the planners down at Plato's Retreat could dream up. Zip has outlasted even the fabulous Siamese twins, who were a favorite until their constant bickering and ill will toward one another undermined their fragile health—if not their crowd appeal.

Not that Zip remembers any of them clearly. He can recall only a limited circle of faces, and then erratically. Clikko the Bushman stays in his mind because, like Zip, Clikko was a pinhead—Zip has never been fond of his own kind. He recalls John Ringling, and a few others among his coworkers. Or are they his employees? He's never sure which. And anyway, what and which among them is worthy of the staggering difficulty of memory?

John Ringling, who like P. T. Barnum before him is nobody's fool, understands Zip's appeal. Easy. Zip is more vulnerable than his other acts because Zip doesn't recognize that he is a freak. Years ago, Barnum convinced Zip that George Washington needed him to perform, that he helped the people who came to see him be happy, and that everyone had the need and the right to be happy. That's why, Barnum told Zip, George Washington crossed the river and cut down the cherry tree. Right.

Zip has since carried this sacred mission to the heart of each performance, peering anxiously into the faces in the crowd to see if he is doing his duty, talking to them as if they are his personal charges.

This quality of Zip's hasn't been without its problems, incidentally. For one thing, he decides periodically that it is he and not Ringling who is in charge of the circus, and he barges about the tent with a stolen cigar in his mouth, making changes. He fires the performers he doesn't like—or whoever else, in his opinion, has failed to please and love the crowds as George Washington intended. Several times he has fired Ringling himself, a practice that might have been troublesome had not Ringling learned to leave the tent in mock tears, staying away until the softhearted Zip begged him to return.

Maybe John Ringling senses a kinship between himself and his diminutive star. Both, in their way, are relics. Barnum and Bailey are long gone, and John is the last of the six Ringling brothers. Whatever the source of his solicitude, he treats Zip well. The pinhead has become a property owner, a landlord, and something of a businessman, too.

That began with Barnum back in the heady days of the 1870s. Zip had been a very large behavior problem then, headstrong and talkative, and if not wise beyond his hat size, at least a man to stand upon his dignity among colleagues and anyone else who crossed his path. During the off-season he presented an even larger headache. Unlike most freaks, who cowered from interaction with the public, Zip enjoyed it and sought it out. From his youth through old age, Zip craved love and companionship. In the early days, he found ways to escape from wherever Barnum kept him. Invariably he would head straight for the street, and on the first corner would begin an impromptu performance—*All the world's a stage,* after all.

These street performances were generally disastrous. Many people recoiled from Zip outside the circus tent, often aggressively so. After Zip suffered a number of brutal beatings, Barnum began to lock his star away from the public when he wasn't performing, more than once in an asylum. But one year, remembering where he originally discovered his star, Barnum farmed Zip out, literally, to a chicken farmer in New Jersey.

For Zip, the farm was paradise. He developed an instant rapport with the free-pecking Rhode Island Reds. He collected eggs with great agility, fed the hens as needed, and kept the henhouse comfortably neat if not sterile. To Zip, the ammonia stench of poultry guano was an olfactory treat beyond compare. He rarely left the henhouse except to eat and relieve himself, and had to be dragged away screaming and kicking the following spring, having, of course, completely forgotten his previous occupation and everyone connected with it. It wasn't until Zip was reminded of his duty to George Washington—which he quickly and guiltily recalled—that Barnum was able to get his star to perform.

Barnum sent him back to the farm the next winter, and in succeeding winters. He also began to bank a small allowance against Zip's retirement.

That's right. Until then Zip *wasn't* getting paid. Not a cent. He was a feeble-minded freak and it was still the nineteenth century, a period in our history when workers, children, and women were frankly and viciously exploited. Freaks were one rung below that, treated as little more than livestock. Barnum's allowance was an act of generosity and foresight, not a due recognition of inalienable human rights, of which P. T. Barnum knew little and cared less. He didn't have to bank an allowance for Zip's future, and no one would have predicted by how many years Zip would outlive him. Few freaks survived a decade on his stages.

After Barnum's death and the subsequent takeover of the circus by the Ringlings, John Ringling discovered the fund in Barnum's account books, and continued, for reasons he never explained, to add to it. Then, in 1907, he purchased several acres of farmland for Zip in the countryside he loved, had a large chicken coop built with fenced grounds and a tiny house adjoining the henhouse. He made an arrangement with a nearby farmer to trade Zip's eggs for feed for the chickens and for minimal care for the pinhead himself.

Zip's chickens did remarkably well for him, so much so that the caretaking farmer turned a tidy profit. On his own incentive, Zip kicked a hole between his hut and the henhouse and moved his favorites in with him. If a fox was about, he simply moved into the henhouse and stayed there.

In time, he learned how to care for chicks, and even mastered the precise science of chicken sexing. But he would slaughter no chickens of his own. Instead, he had his caretaker remove the young roosters and the aging hens, telling him to send them "to Barnum"—who, not surprisingly, was now utterly confused in Zip's mind with George Washington, John Ringling, and God.

In a corner of the henhouse, a hen begins to cluck. The clucking rises to a mild crescendo as the hen raises herself to let the egg slide out into the straw. A slow, slow grin of pleasure crosses Zip's face. He names the hen, and then the egg, and forgets both names an instant later.

What does he see? I'm not sure. Zip is eighty years old now, and his eyes are probably as dim as his mind—which is to say, dim in one way of seeing. So what is it he feels? What does he think about?

Certainly he saw and felt warmth, and color. Probably he felt textures and perceived nuance—the soft sheen of feathers, the small quick heart of a hen beating beneath his hand, the blinking sharpness of the hen's eyes. He heard sounds, the creaking of the roof, the low cluckings of his contented birds. Small, precise delights.

If he were to look beyond the coop, perhaps he might have watched a brief morning breeze blitter and twist the last golden leaves in the pale sunlight. Green moss and compost steaming through a blanket of hoarfrost. For him, this is as clear as it gets.

And what is it that you're doing this morning, or I, who believe that we are more importantly human?

Let me ask that another way. What gleaming sense of purpose drives you grinning toward Armageddon, or by what arrogance have you ignored its advance? What in you has been suppressed? What have you suppressed in yourself to please the circus masters? Do you know or care enough about human happiness to imagine why George Washington crossed the river and cut down the cherry tree? What did you see and hear and smell this morning? What did you touch? What did you think in that unique mind you have, and what did you feel in your heart unlike any other?

THE REPTILE MACHINE

On a normal weekday morning not long ago, Margaret Kincaid butchered her two kids in the bathroom of her home.

It wasn't her *home*, exactly. It was a company house she and her husband Norm had been renting since they moved to Sisk Valley eighteen months before, and it was exactly like the other sixteen company houses on the block. The Kincaids moved to Sisk so Norm could work in the pulp mill. He'd been out of work for a couple of years, so like a normal joe he'd jumped at the job.

Norm and Margaret just wanted a normal life. What they got was a tragedy.

Sisk Valley is like a lot of small towns in the Northwest. It has a population of about 15,000, some rough-and-ready lumber workers, a few government bureaucrats. But the majority are people there to make money and get out to a better place. These

---

SOME NOTES ON DETECTIVE METHODS

At a large and crowded franchise hardware store a few days ago, a customer asked a clerk at the gun counter if he could examine one of the 12-gauge shotguns the store had on display. When the clerk handed the customer the weapon, he calmly pulled a shell from his pocket, and pushed it into the chamber. Then he put the shotgun barrel under his chin and blew his brains across the store's twelve-foot ceilings.

days, private ambition and public fears about the condition of the economy operate on equal terms.

Like that of most of those towns, the Sisk economy is based on a single industry—in this case pulpwood processing and logging. There's the usual assortment of franchise outlets—McDonald's, Burger King, Gulf, Speedee Muffler, Safeway, and so forth. On the margins there's some mineral resource extraction, and a bit of prospecting out in the wilderness areas. North of the city is an Indian reserve with a population of close to a thousand.

From the 1950s through the 1970s Sisk Valley grew, and quickly, like every other hinterland town. Since then population, like employment, has declined, due to tech changes in the big industries and the high kill rate in small businesses. Houses are cheap in Sisk, while living conditions are expensive without being rural or isolated—every second house has a satellite dish on the roof and an RV parked in the driveway. The countryside is pretty where it hasn't been logged off, the rivers are still reasonably unpolluted, and the air is clear and clean once you get a few miles beyond the pulp mill.

But this isn't a story about housing in a company town. And it isn't about the picturesqueness of the Wild North. It's a tragedy about why a woman murdered her kids, one with a kink in it.

After Margaret did the kids she made a pot of coffee in the

Awful, isn't it? But what's the real story here? Is it about how crazy the world is getting, about the private psychosis that would cause a man to kill himself in front of hundreds of strangers, or is it merely another illustration of the need for better gun control laws?

It could be about any of those, but those aren't my reasons for relating this gory little interlude in our collective nightmare. It contains, along its margin, a clue to the phenomena this book is trying to track down. The clue is this: after the suicide, the store

SOME NOTES ON DETECTIVE METHODS

kitchen and drank most of it. Then she walked to the living room, turned on the television, and selected the teleshop channel. She squatted down in front of the set, and became a catatonic. She was sitting in front of it, as motionless as a stone, when her husband came home for lunch.

That's where we got involved. Industrial workers just don't come home for lunch. My editor spotted the slipup in the demographics, and assigned me to fly up to Sisk Valley and check it out.

Me? I'm Barry Klein, newspaper reporter. In the trade some people call me Klein the Slime, but that isn't really fair. I'm a perfectly normal guy doing a useful job. My assignment is crime, but with a specific twist. I handle the crime beat, and the handle I use is an attention grabber. I focus on crime victims, not on the criminals, and I'm damned good at my job.

I didn't invent the angle, of course. That's in the tabloid manual. When they shifted my paper to tabloid format a few years back, reducing the page size and print volume and chopping the length of stories, the corporation brought in a raft of the editorial tricks and reporting angles. The format change cut the serious analysis, replacing it with exposés, pictures, and big headlines—which is what the people were demanding. Personally, I can't see what good the analysis ever did. After they cut it,

---

manager closed the outlet for the remainder of the shopping day. When the announcement of the closing was made over the store's public-address system, interrupting the stream of commercial messages it is normally used for, the customers calmly lined up at the cash registers, stoutly refusing to leave before they completed the consumer purchases they'd come there to make.

It would be premature to rant and rave about what the clue might lead us to. It at least ought to be the signal that this is a detective

11

circulation went way up, which saved my job. Now I spend less time researching and more time flying in and out of strange places. That's just fine with me.

My plane arrived in Sisk at two in the afternoon. After an amazing amount of buggering around—claiming my luggage, renting a car, and then sitting in a roadblock waiting for a Cat to clear a jackknifed logging truck—it was close to six before I found the company subdivisions in the hills overlooking the mill. The Kincaid residence wasn't hard to find even though it was nearly identical to the other sixteen houses on the cul-de-sac. I pulled up in the driveway and knocked on the door. Bang, bang. Norm Kincaid opened it, not very wide. I told him who I was and invited myself in. He let me know he didn't want to talk to me or anyone else, but I stuck my foot in the door to let him know I wasn't about to be denied. Hey, I've got a job to do.

Kincaid acted as if he were on drugs. He stared at my foot for at least fifteen seconds before he asked me what it was I wanted to know.

Getting information out of people who've just been thumped isn't always easy. So I've got a number of tricks: Soft soap and Sympathy, the Responsible Reporter, and a couple of others I

---

book, both above and below the line that separates the two texts. So does everyone agree on the characteristics of a conventional detective?

I don't think so. A detective, as business people and other neoconservative pragmatists-in-ascendancy will argue, must have a client. Legitimate existence for a detective—or anyone else—depends on having a client or a customer or a market. Second, they will insist that legitimacy also depends on the detective's having a case to solve on behalf of the client, or at least an

SOME NOTES ON DETECTIVE METHODS

won't mention. I don't like playing hardball, but I will. I decided to start off easy on Kincaid.

"Look," I said. "I'm terribly sorry about what's happened. I know a tragedy like this is always hard to talk about. If I could just have a few minutes of your time."

Kincaid ran his hands through his thinning blond hair, and looked me in the eye as if he were searching for my soul. Kind of reminded me of Richard Widmark for a second. Younger, but the same look. Something hard underneath that grief.

"I don't know much you probably haven't already heard. My kids are dead and my wife's in the hospital, under guard." He put his hand against the door and tried to close it.

"I'd really appreciate getting a more personal angle," I said, wiggling my foot.

Kincaid went back to staring at my foot the same way he'd stared into my eyes. The soul of a good reporter really is that foot in the door, I suppose. He'd figured me out that far.

"Just a few clean details so I can file an accurate story," I told him, shifting into the Responsible Reporter routine. It intimidates most people. "We need balance. Both sides."

"We? Both sides?"

"Your personal story, the inside one, as well as the blotter."

"What blotter?"

---

attractive commodity to offer. Third, they will require a reasonable probability of profit taking.

If I told you that you—the reader—are my client, or that this book is a commodity and you are my customer, would you accept it? Probably you would. But I don't want to move into that track quite so fast. Other possibilities require some elaboration.

For instance, those who believe in the primacy of, er, inner realities will argue that clients don't matter, that a detective is an archetypal figure attempting to uncover the mysterious origins of

"What the police have. It doesn't always tell the full story, you know; what needs to be told but isn't."

He turned his back on me, but left the door open. "Oh," he said. "I thought maybe you wanted to know why Margie did it."

He began to walk away, as if he'd forgotten me. I stepped inside and followed him. "That too," I said.

"Well, I don't know why she did it. And she isn't doing any talking." He bent over the couch and picked up a copy of *TV Guide*.

I snapped the knockdown question at him. "Why did you come home for lunch?"

He turned to stare at me, the *TV Guide* crunched between his fingers. "What? What did you say?"

My editor had been right. The question exposed a raw nerve. From the look on his face, the nerve was very raw indeed. I quickly changed the subject.

"Do you have a picture of your wife and children I could look at?" I asked.

He grimaced, and gestured toward the mantelpiece. There was a five-by-seven color photo of a woman in her thirties. A small blond girl of about seven stood beside her, soldierlike, while a boy, about three years old and also blond, sat on her knee. A half-dozen other family photos littered the mantelpiece.

---

individual sexual and social alienation. Although they probably wouldn't recognize it, they probably believe that detectives operate beyond the rules of mainstream economic activity—like themselves, excluded from day-to-day limitations by privilege or obsessive predilection.

In their minds, therefore, the detective is primarily his own client, a prisoner, victim, and projectile of his or her own subconscious or unconscious motivations. In their view, what matters most is the origin and pedigree of the case, which is *always* about the origins of criminality. Professionals in the field will

SOME NOTES ON DETECTIVE METHODS

"Coffee?" he asked.

"Sure," I said. "Thanks." As he left the room I stepped over to the mantelpiece and rearranged the photographs. There were several pieces of bric-a-brac—the largest icon was a ceramic black panther, nearly a foot long. There were also several Dresden dolls, probably Taiwanese imitations. I slipped the five-by-seven, still in the frame, into my briefcase and sat down.

He returned from the kitchen carrying two mugs and placed them on the coffee table next to a large glass ashtray. The coffees were already creamed, and, I suspected, sugared.

"I put creamer in it," he said. "Artificial. She, uh, Margaret . . ."

I like coffee black, but I didn't say so. It was instant coffee, so it would've tasted like mud no matter what he put in it.

". . . She likes it that way," I said, finishing the sentence for him as I scanned the room. "What else does she like?"

I wasn't really expecting an answer. Just fishing. The room wasn't giving me much. Light shag carpet, tartan couch and chair, no bookcases, a 26-inch Sony, fairly new. In the corner beside it lay a dozen or so thumbed-through *Guides*.

"She doesn't read much, eh?" I asked.

"Some magazines," he answered, gesturing without thinking

---

sing (in chorus with chromatic harmonies) that at the center of each and all of us rages the Oedipal struggle between incest and otherness.

I can't argue successfully against that because the struggle they're talking about is inherent in the human condition. But I have difficulty believing that we're all essentially fucked up, and that most of us are crazy at heart. Even if I did believe it, I'd have to point out that lunacy and productivity haven't ever been enemies, whether the madness is fueled by Oedipal sublimation, too many drugs, or bolts that've shaken loose and dropped into the gears. If

15

at the Sony. "She watched television. This one's new. We have a portable in the bedroom."

"What's her favorite show?"

I knew I'd short-circuited his brain stem when he looked up as if the question were puzzling to him. "I don't know. She watches this and that. Everybody watches television around here. She's here all day with nothing to do. She was here alone."

Several more circuits kicked into his main conduit. He tried to shut them out, but it was easy to see he was going to fail. I opened it up more without thinking. Instinct. A good reporter operates on instinct. Just a step away from a core reflex, but the distinction is important.

"She was here all alone?" I asked. "In what sense? What about the kids?"

"They're dead."

"I know. I'm sorry. But until yesterday they were alive. What did she do, with the children? I mean, before she . . . harmed them."

"She was always good with them. Kind. She loved those kids. . . ." He drifted off into a sob.

I was losing him too soon. "I'm trying to get things straight, Mr. Kincaid. You're not being very cooperative."

He looked up, surprised. "Christ," he mumbled, "my wife's

I try to make a world out of what these people take for reality, it just gets too damned bumpy and inverted. It might explain the presence of 20,000 nuclear warheads on the planet, but it doesn't have anything constructive to say about how to get rid of them.

There's a world around our minds, and our bodies are in it all day and all night. Something won't let me forget that reality has a pragmatic existence if not a philosophically secure one. Since I'm committed to the idea that no superior, omniscient, and omnipotent being, force, or concept of being is pulling our strings, I have

SOME NOTES ON DETECTIVE METHODS

locked up in a hospital room, my kids are dead, and you're asking me to be more cooperative?"

"You do want people to get the right idea about this," I cajoled.

His eyes narrowed and I glimpsed a deep river of rage a split second before it burst its banks. He began to curse, and for a second or two I thought he might go for me. That's happened more than once. I suppressed an adrenal shiver and told myself it was scalpel time—time to really open him up. I shook my pen over the notepad in my lap, and made as if to write something down. That paralyzes most people.

It worked, but not quite the way I wanted. He quietened, but the anger remained, a hot dark current in his eyes.

"Get out!" he hissed. "Get out of my fucking house, or I'll throw you out on your goddamned ear."

I stood up. What the hell, I thought. No sense in challenging a man who might just be a lunatic. I mean, every individual's expression of grief is different. You scalpel a guy, and you might find a sheep or a harmless lizard inside him, but you also might free a genuine Nile croc. There's no absolute way of knowing which it'll be. If this man's grief made him into a croc, it sure as hell had enough to swim around in. I'd seen that.

"I know you're hiding something, Kincaid," I said as he pushed me out the door. "I'm going to find out what it is."

---

to insist that we—you and I—are damned well responsible for all of this, or at least liable. We can blame our private and collective histories, and we can blame our parents or our reproductive and masturbatory impulses, but it won't get us out of the collective mess we're in.

And anyway, we're talking about detectives, not Armageddon. Other ways of looking at detectives demand consideration. For instance, the folks in television production will point out that whether or not a detective has a client is irrelevant. Detectives exist because the public has a democratic—or is it a

He slammed the door hard enough to crack the glass panel to the left of the door. I stood there and listened to him bash the furniture around. Tsk, tsk.

My investigation of Norman Kincaid began in earnest the next morning, right after I Air Expressed the photo of his wife and kids to my editor. The photo ran in the morning edition along with a filler story to keep the pot boiling. Standard practice.

As soon as I sent the packet off I headed for the nearest computer terminal. I have semilegal access to a series of data bases, and I'm no saint about using them. A story is a story, and over the next hour I used them to strip the disguises from Kincaid.

First I accessed his motor vehicle and police records. Nothing much in the MV records—a couple of speeding tickets a few years back, a seat-belt violation, one failing to stop citation. No liability claims against his insurance. Very clean, I thought to myself. The credit check revealed the flakiness of someone who's been unemployed, and there were no life-insurance policies.

The police records were loaded. Not with quantity, but with quality. The first item was from back East, a statutory rape charge when Kincaid was twenty. That had been dropped, but was followed by a couple of drunk and disorderly convictions over

---

demographic—right to vicarious action and adventure. The craving for a paying client, they would say, is silly historical residue. The advertisers pay for everything. The profits go to the network and its advertisers, and the public buys the right products and has an entertaining day if not a nice one, which is what life is about, no? They will then lose interest in the entire topic and demand that the goddamned action proceed.

One last item. If I were an academic theorist of detective fiction writers like John D. MacDonald or Mickey Spillane, I would insist that a detective must maintain a private contract with reality, an

SOME NOTES ON DETECTIVE METHODS

the next several years, each from a different location. Kincaid got around in those days. There were a couple of trespassing charges he got off on, and two assault and battery charges that'd been dropped, right around what I deduced were his wandering days. And then just six months back, a hooker charge, a conviction with a $500 fine. Bingo.

I headed back to Kincaid's house. He wasn't there so I drove over to the hospital. I figured he'd be with his wife. I'd phoned the hospital just before midnight to check on her condition. No change. I managed to twist an off-the-record "no change expected" comment out of the nurse. She told me the doctors thought Margaret Kincaid had mixed some drugs, and the feeling was that she'd wacked herself hard enough to cause serious brain damage. The catatonic act, in other words, wasn't an act at all.

Kincaid was at the hospital, standing outside the windowed observation unit with a duty officer. They weren't talking. The officer was reading a Stephen King paperback, and Kincaid had his nose pressed to the surface of the one-way glass, gazing at his wife. I voiced in that image on my minirecorder before I approached him

All the innocence went out of his face the moment he saw me. "What do you want?" he snapped.

---

interior reality that maintains, on its outskirts, a sentimental landscape with conventionally needy clients and a readily visible criminal climate. Further, I'd insist, as a student of formalist technology, that this contract remain unexplicit, on the grounds that it is the detective's idiosyncratic vision that creates the fictional élan and produces the unpredictable predictability—the "pursuit of the ineffable" so dear to industrial formalists of literature.

The world doesn't offer such comforting support systems these days, and I see no reason why literature should. There's no stable criminal element out there, and no stable advertisers. For litera-

I snapped right back. "Did your wife know about your recent brush with the law?"

This time he surprised me. "Yes," he said, "she did. She knew about everything I did. Now get the hell out of here before I do something we'll both regret."

The police officer motioned for me to leave. I considered making a scene, but judging from the look on the officer's face, I figured he'd arrest me instead of Kincaid. Small towns.

Speaking of small towns, Sisk Valley was turning out to be a particularly lurid little dump. The night before Margaret Kincaid killed her children, two native Indians—a father and daughter—poisoned themselves in an isolated cabin about seventy miles north of Sisk. Probably a drinking party of some sort. If the story runs to type, they were probably drinking methyl alcohol or dry-cleaning fluid. But the fact that it was a father/daughter situation made it potentially kinky. And the victims weren't your run-of-the-mill natives, either. The father was a big wheel on the reservation, and comparatively wealthy.

I decided to let Kincaid stew in his own juices for a while, so I dropped down to the police station to get the story on the poisoned Indians. I figured I might be able to write it into a nice little scare-story about alcohol abuse and wasted lives.

---

ture, the stable audience has dissipated, gone to television or merely gotten old. The stable forms are gone, even though a shrinking consumer submarket props up the shattered remnants.

This is the Global Village, where private vision is obsolete and the multinational banks ensure that nothing is free. Crimes are being committed here, and not just the sensational kinds we've become inured to. These are crimes against history, discourse, and the privacy of the mind.

Using whatever tools of language and cognitive science that can be earned, stolen, or borrowed, the detective in this book is

SOME NOTES ON DETECTIVE METHODS

Damned if the story wasn't a minor beaut. The substance abuse angle would do nicely. The police weren't bothering with an autopsy. They'd flown a coroner up to examine the bodies. He'd poked around a bit, decided it was accidental, probably the Sterno he found in the cabin. They left the bodies for the band to bury, some sort of local custom. I read through the coroner's preliminary report, and decided to drive out to the reservation to see if there was anything interesting he'd missed.

There wasn't much. A reservation spokesman called it a tragedy, and said it shouldn't have happened, and so forth, and so forth. The only unusual bit of information he gave me was that the young woman had apparently been involved for some time with a white man, but he either didn't know who it was or wasn't saying. I wrote the story and filed it electronically. It wasn't big news, just filler.

It was just after one in the afternoon, still too early for another shot at Kincaid, so I tapped into the system to see what it had on Margaret Kincaid.

What came out wasn't exactly the standard profile of a housewife who comes unraveled in an isolated community. First of all, she had a university degree—she was, in fact, a registered pharmacist. She'd practiced for about five years before she got married and had kids. The MV and police records turned up

---

going to make an existential investigation of the regions of human experience that operate prior to or outside the transformation of human reality into commercial commodities, where what is local hasn't yet lost its capacity to generate sensibility and perspective.

There's a slight peculiarity to the detection methods I'll use, but it isn't a literary trick. It's this: my private authorial goal will be the same as the public ones of my narrator: to locate the propelling and governing agency of the Global Village, to elucidate where it has invaded the self, and to dramatize how and by what means it now operates.

21

nothing, but when I checked the Pharmaceutical College an interesting blip showed up.

Seems she'd been fired from one job and reprimanded by the college because a number of lethal substances had gone missing on her responsibility. The investigation—if one was carried out—was inconclusive. I found myself wondering, with that kind of knowledge, why she hadn't poisoned the kids instead of chopping them up. Certainly less messy. But it was now a solid probability that her catatonic state was chemically induced. She'd have known what to take.

Things were getting more interesting, but I still didn't have the answer to the question of why Norm Kincaid came home for lunch. I did, however, have a couple of prods. I reread my notes, logged off the data base, and drove over to Kincaid's house.

His car wasn't in the driveway, but I pulled in and parked, thinking he might have parked somewhere else and was hiding. He wasn't there, but the door was unlocked. What the hell, I thought.

I started in the bedroom. There were two surprises there, one small, the other large. The small surprise was that one of them had an interest in native art. A carved mask hung above the bed, and several other objects were scattered around the room. I don't know anything about native art, but at least I could

---

No altruism is involved here. Acting in one's own private interest was never *really* workable, even though generation after generation has acted as if it were. It only appears to have worked. If you want to know why it doesn't work in the long term, imagine what kind of world your grandchildren will have—or try to imagine great-grandchildren.

Private and public can't be separated, and I'm not going to continue to uphold the delusion that they can, however cherished it may be. My fate as a detective, writer, and/or citizen is tied to that of everyone else, here and now. Whatever the future holds is

SOME NOTES ON DETECTIVE METHODS

tell these weren't manufactured in Taiwan. Definitely local and authentic.

The large surprise was under the bed. Norm Kincaid was packed to leave. Two suitcases, one packed with clothes, the other, strangely, with camping gear—a compass, fishing lures, line, an expensive knife, some antibiotics, rain clothes. In the basement, also packed, were several rifles, some ammunition, an arctic sleeping bag, a large fishing net, and a metal box that appeared to contain a kind of chemistry set.

I was coming up the basement stairs when Kincaid burst through the front door. "What do you think you're doing?" he demanded, obviously trying to keep his temper under control. I had to think fast.

"The door was open, Mr. Kincaid," I said. "I assumed you'd found my note and left it open for me."

"What note? What are you talking about?"

"I left a note last night asking you to be here at two P.M. When I got here I figured you'd just stepped out and were coming back soon." I'd left no such note, of course, but he wouldn't know that.

"What were you doing down there?"

"Looking around," I said. "Trying to gather some color for my story. I didn't think you'd mind."

---

now pervasive, an absolute and collective fate, albeit still mysterious in its specifics. If a fate awaits our world, we're all going to meet it pretty much together, and before great-grandchildren can be born.

In the simplest possible terms, I'm trying to create a "case"—a context—within which the present human condition can be defined, and within which the human species can redefine itself, relocate some of its values and priorities, and hopefully, begin to understand itself in an information-overloaded environment.

Here, just for a moment, I begin to resemble a traditional

"I sure as hell do mind. You people don't have the right to ransack private homes."

"Planning a trip, I see," I interrupted. That slowed him down, but only for a moment.

"I do a lot of camping," he said. "Nothing criminal about being ready." His anger had subsided. He was becoming unsure, defensive.

"Ready for what? And where?"

Kincaid shrugged. "Upriver. I've got a claim up beyond the Indian lands. As a matter of fact I was headed up there just before . . ."

He came to a solid stop, sat down on the top step, and sighed. "Okay," he said. "I've got a hot claim. Really hot. And I was going to spend a couple of weeks up there."

Once he'd told me one thing, I knew he'd spill the rest. Things were dropping into place. "Did your wife know you were going?"

"She found out. She also figured out I was quitting my job at the mill."

"You were?"

"Yes."

"Did she agree with that?"

"Obviously not," he answered, almost sarcastically.

"It doesn't quite add up," I said.

---

detective: the moment I misread the evidence, I will have lost the trail. It will become my personal fiction, easily classified and disarmed, a bright taxonomic pin through its spine to paralyze it, and an ocean of critical formaldehyde to preserve it for a future generation of scholars and investigators who don't interest me because they may not get to be born. Most important, it wouldn't be anything you'd recognize.

That's why, from the start, you're going to have to put up with a shadow game over who the narrator is, and when he's a detective

SOME NOTES ON DETECTIVE METHODS

"If you knew what Margie and I have been through, it would. Look," he said, now almost pleading. "I'll tell you, but you can't print it."

I said nothing. He continued on anyway.

"Like I said, the claim's hot. Gold. Maybe a major find. Margie didn't want me to go for it. Too risky, she said. I could see her point of view, sort of. I used to be a rounder, always jumping for a chance for the big score. She'd gotten me out of too many scrapes before—never mind the details—"

"I know some of the details," I interjected. "What you don't tell me I'll find out from others in the end. This is your chance to tell it right, so keep talking."

"Anyway, I'd been keeping fairly straight for almost ten years. We'd had our ups and downs, like. I guess when I got the job here she figured it would be straight sailing." His voice turned rueful. "I guess I didn't quite see how much that meant to her."

I thought about the way she'd killed the children, and had to suppress a shudder. "That's an understatement," I said.

His eyes clouded again for a moment, but it was hard to tell what he was thinking. He might have been thinking about her, or about what she'd done to the kids. I dunno what goes on in people's heads. Maybe he was angry, maybe he was sad, or maybe he was just hoping he could think his way out of it all.

---

solving a case and when he's just a writer trying to make sense of the world. The soft boundary between documentation, imaginative invention, malicious fallacy, and outright browbeating is going to get blurred.

Barry Klein claims he's just an ordinary guy doing his job—a cog in a big machine. He believes in the demographic norms (no pun intended) his machine sets out to enlarge and manipulate. Apparently, he shares its values without thinking about their conse-

25

"Well, okay," he said finally. "You won't print this part?"

"I'd have to have a very, very good reason," I said. "I'm a journalist. The public has a right to know. You know I'll get to the bottom line, with or without your help."

"But the claim will get swarmed," he said. "I could lose it. I need time . . ."

"That's a different story," I said coldly. "Keep talking."

"Well, look," he said, his eyes suddenly calculating, "how about we go right to the bottom line? What if I cut you in? If it assays, that is. I'll split the claim with you."

I made my own calculation. I had a good enough story. My editor would demand the original lunchtime angle, but he'd never be the wiser if I just wrote it up as a worried husband with superior instincts—ones that cut in a few minutes late. I could juice the rest of it up enough to satisfy the system. And I'd brought in the other story about the suicides, so the trip had developed some additional local copy, enough to keep the system humming for a few days. If Kincaid's claim didn't pan out, I could track him later on.

"How do I know I can trust you?" I said.

"A private agreement," he said. "Nothing registered. But don't worry—it'll hold up in court if the claim goes big."

We drew up the document on his kitchen table, and Kincaid

---

quences. Maybe he doesn't care about any of it. Maybe he doesn't think about such things at all—he just likes the identity and life-style it provides, and that's enough.

There's nothing *unusual* about him, but there are two things about him that are dangerous. First, he's forgotten Nuremberg's essential lesson: that individuals must remain critical of any and all authority. Barry Klein has recapitulated Adolf Eichmann's defense of his actions at Auschwitz.

That might be forgivable except that as a newspaper reporter Klein is a front-line Information Age cultural worker. He's on the

SOME NOTES ON DETECTIVE METHODS

agreed to get in touch with me monthly to file a progress report. Two hours later I filed the following story, and three hours after that I was on the plane out of Sisk Valley.

TOTS BUTCHERY ALMOST AVERTED

Sisk Valley, scene of the brutal murders of two children three days ago, is still at a loss to explain the actions of housewife Margaret Kincaid. Kinkaid, 36, bludgeoned and then dismembered her daughter Julie, 7, and son Mark, 3, on the morning of June 5. The tragedy was almost averted by her worried husband Norman, who left his job at the mill to return home early, arriving home just minutes too late to save them.

Kincaid, a boiler maintenance supervisor at Sisk Valley Pulp and Paper, has stated that he knew his wife was depressed, but couldn't say why. "I had no idea she would do this," he told the *Observer* in an exclusive interview. "I don't understand it. I simply can't imagine how anyone could do such a thing. I've lost everything."

Mrs. Kincaid, who has not spoken since the slayings, is under psychiatric care in Sisk Valley General Hospital pending transference to a prison forensic unit for further psychiatric evaluation. An inquest will be held into the deaths next week. No criminal proceedings have been launched pending the results of the inquest.

---

leading edge of a political culture and economy that loudly claims that its success depends on the quality and flow of information—read accuracy of data and the efficiency of the structure in which it is lodged. Klein's job is to interpret and disseminate the raw data of social and political life for other people. To have absolved himself of responsibility to act in the best interest of his readers is an act of serious moral turpitude. This man is an uncritical agent of authority, and he doesn't give a shit if anyone knows.

I don't like him. But that's not the crucial point. You might be

Kincaid phoned in his first progress report right when he said he would. He hadn't done much by then—there'd been the funeral for the kids, and the various hearings that determined what to do with his wife. She'd managed to fry her brain completely, so she was quietly boxed away in an institution for the criminally insane. Kincaid said he was going up to the claim the following week, and would send news by month's end.

I never got the second report. He was killed in a freak accident two weeks later. Apparently a falling tree landed on his boat and crushed him while he was on the river. A couple of native guys who were with him found the body downstream several hours later, so it was no disappearing act. What the hell, I figured, nothing ventured, nothing gained. I wrote a cleanup story and fed it into the system.

MORE TRAGEDY IN SISK VALLEY

Norman Kincaid, 42, whose wife Margaret butchered their children six weeks ago, was killed in a tragic riverboating accident Monday. Witnesses state that the heavily clothed Kincaid was knocked from the boat by an overhanging tree branch, and had no chance once in the water. His body was recovered several hours later by companions.

Residents of Sisk Valley are planning a memorial fund to help victims of similar tragedies in the future. Margaret Kincaid remains under psychiatric care locally.

---

wondering why I haven't presented a more virtuous journalistic investigator—say Bob Woodward, or a cooked-up latter-day Sherlock Holmes. Well, there's a more important problem than Klein's character and skills or his moral indifference and his relativism. That problem is the machine Klein is working for. It's this machine I want to expose at the beginning.

Let's call it the "Reptile Machine." Everyone, according to the tabloid logic system Klein operates, is a potential crime victim. He'd cheerfully tell you the reason crime reporting fills so much

AKRON DESIGN CENTER ANTIDOTES
Communications and Public Information

a: Broadcast telecommunications and print media must be locally owned by public corporations. Fifty percent of management teams must be PUS draftees selected by lottery.

b: Television programming originating from a distance of farther than one thousand miles must be unsupported by commercials.

c: Satellite receiving dishes will be prohibited to ensure that the imaginative and informational lives of citizens in a given location have a local base rather than (as now) in Atlanta, New York, or other current meganetwork source locations.

d: Televising of violent individual or antagonist sports such as boxing, tennis, and competitive aerobics will be prohibited.

e: Live broadcasting of baseball's World Series, professional hockey's Stanley Cup finals, and other team sports championship series or games are permitted, along with away games of local teams.

f: Subject matter of interviews with professional athletes can treat anything except sports.

g: All radio programming will be produced locally, on a rationale similar to that in c:) above.

h: No actor or actress involved in an advertisement—particularly television commercials—will be allowed to wash or to change clothing in the twenty-four hours prior to filming or recording. This

---

of the news is that paranoia and dread sell papers. Like the people who produce our television fare, he'd probably trot out some slogans about the democracy of the bottom line, the people get what the people demand, blah, blah.

Hardly. Paranoia and dread are the chief output of the Reptile Machine. And since we live with a legal apparatus that allows no one to go through a single day without transgressing the law in some casual way, we're all criminals. What counts is the degree of criminality.

will ensure that the product images created will more closely resemble the people and conditions they attempt to manipulate. Use of cosmetic makeup is strictly prohibited.

i: Seventy percent of newspaper copy will be produced locally, and 100 percent of journalistic analysis must originate locally. Magazine journalism is excluded from this provision.

j: To ensure that news coverage has a more enlightened purpose than to make us all want to crawl under the bed and stay there, writers of any story concerning violence or misadventure must be filmed or photographed lying *underneath* either the victim(s), the perpetrator, or the technological device used to perpetrate the violence (provided that the device is physically larger than the victims or perpetrators).

k: To foster greater respect for precision in public communication of all kinds, and to further public education, roving three-person Truth in Advertising (TIA) panels will be selected by lottery from the PUS draft.

TIA panels will have a mandate to improve levels of accuracy in public communication, and will have the right to intervene in any profit-oriented communicative event with translations of their own devising. Television, radio, and newspaper ads and copy, government and corporate reports and brochures, and public gatherings of all kinds will be subject to intervention. Advertisers subjected to TIA interventions must extend contracted runs of ads by fourteen days without right of appeal.

l: *Banning opinion polls:* Processes that respond to a wider view

---

But we're merely *potential* victims. And because victims are all one kind—innocent victims—we've grown more afraid of being violated than of being the violators.

Motivational and marketing psychology figured this out decades ago. It's what the tabloid manual has been built around. Someone recognized that as civilization's infrastructure became more incomprehensible and complex, human beings would return to a reliance on the reptilian core of the brain to keep themselves in balance.

The reptilian core is the part of the spinal cord that extends into

SOME NOTES ON DETECTIVE METHODS

of the human community than those accessed through the reptilian core are needed, procedures that enable the resumption of public service and long-range calculations and allow for a future. As a primary conduit of reptilian core stimulus, opinion polling will be unconditionally banned.

m: *Reducing political propaganda:* Government advertising of any kind will be banned, unless the elected ministerial chief involved appears in the advertisement without clothing. If television or radio is involved, the official must appear without the aid of TelePrompTers or prepared written texts.

n: *Binding campaign promises:* Governments will be elected on the basis of legally binding program proposals. Each proposal will be time-limited, and failure to implement would constitute grounds for dissolution of the government. Any change in programs in excess of 1 percent of the government's annual budget would be subject to ratification either by referendum or by general election.

---

the brain like a kind of reactive claw. It's called the reptilian core because it's all the brain a reptile has. If you watch reptiles, you'll see that their perceptual operating system processes all information paranoically—everything is either a potential or actual threat to security. And if you check the environments reptiles prefer, they're invariably of the low-information variety. In downtown New York, your average alligator or iguana would have a brain-circuit blowout in about ninety seconds. The human paranoia threshold is further off, but it can be stimulated almost as easily as a reptile's. And the Reptile Machine is the apparatus that does it.

THE AKRON DESIGN CENTER

I'm Public Eye, your guide to the Akron Design Center. I'm not Barry Klein, and I'm not like him. I don't work for the authorities, and I'm not a private detective. You can't hire me to find out if your wife or lover is cheating on you, and I'm not interested in keeping the streets safe for property owners. If a beautiful blond with a white Cadillac convertible offered me bushels of money to find her ghostly father, I'd tell her to take a hike.

I don't harbor secret desires, and I don't care about yours. I'm convinced that our secret desires don't belong to us anymore. Or if and when they do, they're irrelevant to the case I'm on. That's one thing the Akron Design Center and I agree on: there's nothing to secrets that implicate only one person. From there we diverge again.

I spend a lot of time staring at landfill sites and wall graffiti, gazing at barbed- and razor-wired compounds, walking along

---

The Reptile Machine creates artificially stimulating perceptual environments that require steadily increased levels of security and protection to ward off steadily less tangible threats. The perceptual devices used are referred to as "the Claw"—they close the reptilian core around the human brain, reducing the average citizen to a paranoid iguana wondering where the next attack will come from.

You'll recognize the elements—the fingers, as it were—of the Claw right away. The standby is "the Maniac." There's one in the alley behind your house right now. If not, consider yourself lucky.

SOME NOTES ON DETECTIVE METHODS

deserted roads, staring at polluted ditches or ill-identified industrial installations. My job is to wonder why we live, and how we will continue to live.

It's depressing, as you can imagine. Underneath the slimy skin of compulsory business optimism, confidence tricks, and claims of efficiency, unanswered questions teem like maggots over a decomposing body.

The city of Akron resembles a hundred other contemporary cities in the North American hinterland. Three hundred thousand people live there, many depressed and unhappy, wondering if maybe they should pack up and move somewhere else, maybe New York or California. The center of the city is in what urban planners used to call urban decay and now refer to as redevelopment opportunities. The people who live there are mostly poor, ethnic, black, or combinations of those three. There is some redevelopment renewal going on—old buildings becoming parking lots, a square block of tenements wakes up to discover that it is a huge and windowless warehouse. Shopping malls named after trees that don't grow anywhere near Akron are constantly promised and quietly canceled shortly after elections. Those that are built are identical to ten thousand other malls across the continent, with glassed-in galleries to keep

---

The Maniac gets at least one person per city per week. For the times when the Maniac is sleeping, the tabloid papers run their backlist of articles explaining what the Maniac is and does, and why. That usually cracks a few screws loose in someone, and the Maniac is back in business.

People used to feel safe sending their kids to school, so "the Molester" was invented. Now, you send your kids to school knowing that every teacher may be dying to diddle them. But the social workers love this one, since it's opened whole new entrepreneurial fields for them—exposing molesters and

out the local pollution. They're filled with dazed consumers pawing over franchised merchandise manufactured off-continent, and they're run by bright-eyed polyester managers who wear name tags but don't want to know your name except to put it on their junk-mail list. Life goes on, mostly sideways or down.

Thirty years ago most of the automobile tires produced in America were manufactured in or near Akron. They called Akron "Tiretown." You could get a job in one of those filthy tire factories, and if you worked hard and smart, you could own your own home, have five or six kids, and maybe get to be a department foreman. After work you could drink any of a dozen brands of watery beer and get your face pushed in at well over a dozen tough bars. Living or working in Akron meant that you were close enough to feel the pulse of America's heartland.

They closed the last tire factory a few years ago. Now when people talk "Tiretown" they mean the franchise corporation that retails tires across North America. The tires are made somewhere else now—Taiwan or Korea, where manual labor is cheaper and the workers don't bring class-action suits against the company when they start to die from industrially inflicted cancers. The tire companies of Akron moved the workers out and the managers and researchers in long ago. They spin profits in and

---

then recovering and rebuilding the kids.

Another one is "the Plague." Plagues are as old as the hills, but the Reptile Machine has updated the concept. The current ones have a quasi-scientific basis. Cancer is the standby. An easy one, since science has demonstrated that any substance interfaced with or ingested by the human body in sufficient quantities is carcinogenic. Right now, cancer, along with nukes and a half-dozen hybrids of the two are all on standby for the currently hot item: immune system collapse—read AIDS—or the slightly less lethal nonsexual equivalent, Epstein-Barr virus. Both would have

SOME NOTES ON DETECTIVE METHODS

out of town, country, and hemisphere electronically, and they *think* about the market for tire products.

There's massive low-level unemployment in Akron, but not noticeably more than in the rest of the hinterland. Some people leave and go to the big cities, but most hang around and get overweight on junk food. They get drunk too much and depressed and generally less and less employable. If they don't get sent to jail for beating up their wives and kids, they get reclassified out of the unemployment stat files—chronic welfare cases, unemployables, part of the growing fringe of the homeless and disenfranchised—the failures who are never counted accurately because the failure is in the system that put them into the count.

The managers and researchers who remain live in the new "secure" residential developments out on the farmlands around Akron. They do all right for themselves, moving on up the corporate ladder, as the saying goes, and eventually out of Akron.

Most tourists would take the first bus out of Akron. Not me. I've got questions to ask. How did all this mediocrity get created, anyway? What's happening to Akron, Ohio? Is there anything under that impermeable, inorganic, nondecaying skin of white plastic that's settled over it?

Akron, Ohio, has "made in America" stamped all over it, even if the America meant is in Canada, Korea, Taiwan, Japan, or

---

us all living inside full-body condoms. At the other pole, just so we know there's no escape, there's also a significant increase in immune system hyperactivity. Instead of breaking down, the immune system goes on red alert and becomes allergic to everything, including itself.

Without disputing whatever reality any of these have—and they always have some—they're a wonderful medium for social control, and an even better generator of new commodities and services. The generating principle is always the same: a frightened organism will react simplistically, predictably, and conser-

even Russia. Those are accomplice states in a union most Americans are no longer part of, least of all the hard-drinking, balding, potbellied kick-fag tire workers of Akron, Ohio. They're ghosts of the past. So are most of the rest of us.

If you still think, as people could as recently as twenty years ago, that the United States is the center of the world, or that the United States of America means the same thing as America, it's time to wake up. The only center America has now is the Akron Design Center, and you're probably not part of it. You've been globalized. Your old political rights as a citizen have been marginalized into consumer rights, and the Akron Design Center *demands* that you exercise them.

We all live in the same economic and cultural community now, and we all reap its benefits and face its depredations, whether we're a grocer in Brighton, England, a tribesman pulling nets from the waters of the Trobriand Islands, or a writer eking out a living in New York City. We're subjected to the same kinds of manipulations. Intensities vary, but the messages reach all of us now, and they're all the same.

Oh, sure, you may enjoy being a consumer, and you might mistake it for a good and decent life. But no one leads an independent life now, save by corporate privilege, accident, inherited wealth, or simple and probably temporary luck. No one leads an

---

vatively. A frightened iguana will leap onto or into anything if it's convinced that the refuge is safer than where it is. The Reptile Machine creates the Claw, wraps it around your brain, and then designs the escape hatches and landing pads for the consumer corporations or any other institution or person with the money to buy one. When you try to leap to safety, they're waiting to greet you on arrival.

I've got a very simple character test I run on people when they make me uneasy, as Barry Klein does. I imagine that we're in Nazi

SOME NOTES ON DETECTIVE METHODS

unmanipulated life. We're consumers first now, citizens second, and the difference gets greater every day.

Here's my cognitive problem: How do you *detect* this in a meaningful way? It's wall-to-wall subliminals, disinformation aimed and overloading our receptor circuits, deliberate diseducation. The Center develops social technologies to universalize consumer demand, and when these technologies become truly efficient, they will rid the system of individualized demand. It is breaking down every form of unprogrammed volition, prying into human motivational circuitry so we can be turned on a dime and either altered to conform or be eliminated.

I grew up in Akron, and I was a helpless witness to its transformation. But as all children do if given a chance, I also thought it was the earthly paradise. I had a mother and a grandmother who held me in their arms and showed me how roses grow and why birds sing. My grandmother believed that the beautiful, voracious, winged dead are all around us. When I asked how that could be, she explained that the rain was the tears of the dead, sad that they couldn't be alive anymore, and that when I felt a breeze against my face it might be from the beating of their wings. Angels, she called them.

My mother believed in invisible powers too, but for her they were different, less tangible, and more troubled. When I begged

---

Germany between, say, the spring of 1938 and the summer of 1939. Then I ask myself what the person under scrutiny would be doing.

Not much doubt about what Barry Klein would be up to, is there? My calculation is that he wouldn't be a writer at all. He'd have been in the SS since about 1935, working his way up, but not too far. How about Norm Kincaid? He's a little more difficult to place. He's older than Klein for one thing, a slightly more complex figure for another. Where was he in the mid-1920s, or earlier? Was he sowing his wild oats across the Munich barricades,

38

her to show me what an angel looked like, she took me to a cemetery and showed me the angels there. I remember just one of them, at least seven feet tall, with enormous outspread wings. It was made from concrete and it was cradling a child in its arms. My mother pointed to its uplifted face, which was already beginning to corrode from the acid mists from the factories.

"There is trouble even for angels," she said. Then she told me who I was, and why I'd been born.

I studied any and everything that passed my way, provided that it promised to tell me something about how life—and Akron— was changing—why the angels were in trouble. I studied primitive cultures and their mythologies and customs, modern architecture, forestry, computer design. I worked as an urban planner, as a teacher in every odd circumstance I could force my way into—anything that would provide evidence of the destruction of my legacy. And I discovered that practically everything offered evidence.

Take architecture. It's easy to glimpse the dimensions of the Akron Design Center in architecture. Architecture is the most visible nexus of deliberate design and subliminal economic motivations we have. As far back as the early 1950s, evidence of cloned design concepts began to appear in residential subdivision design, and they occurred in areas as environmentally and so-

---

and on which side? Where has he been since? Where will he drift in the next few years? Which opportunity will he seize next? And what about Margaret Kincaid? Without her television set, her brain bombers, and her *TV Guides*, what would she become? They're each dead ends, despite the presence of extraordinary historical resonances each character exudes.

The *Medea* of Euripides, for instance, written during the last half of the fifth century B.C., depicts Medea's response to her husband Jason's attempt to divorce her in order to marry the daughter of Creon, king of Corinth, after ten years of marriage and

SOME NOTES ON DETECTIVE METHODS

cially diverse as Jackson, Mississippi, and Edmonton, Alberta. Design features aimed at accommodating local social characteristics and habits, climate, light orientation, and material availability disappeared. They were replaced by repetitive "life-style" features that enforce certain types of casual interactions and prevent others. Construction practices changed to reward large-scale production and demographic projections.

Decorative features—such as A-frame entrance gables meant to divert alpine-depth snow loads—started appearing in areas that never see snow, supplanting local and more accurate responses to landscape and climate characteristics. The Akron Design Center made housing into an expression of solidarity with global demographic and occupational ideals—a "world" society that ignores the local conditions and values of Jackson and Edmonton alike. Artificial structural patterns were also introduced, such as compact kitchens that reinforce the division of domestic labor and serve "efficiencies" that often alienate residents from local practices and simple domestic contact.

I could cite evidence like this until we're all nauseous. Look around you. Your new house has been engineered, but not for you. But I'll never convince you this way, will I? Okay, I'll stop, for now, and tell you stories. Here's one that starts right in Akron.

---

two children. In so doing, Jason commits several grave errors. He abandons his children in a hostile environment and breaks the political and emotional bond with the formidable and passionate Medea.

Medea, who saved Jason's life several times while he was on the Argonaut adventure that made him famous, retaliates in measure. A professional poisoner by trade, she constructs a beautiful but poisonous dress and diadem for Jason's bride-to-be, and feigns acceptance of her husband's betrayal to convince him to take the poisoned articles to the vain young woman. Medea asks

I'd just gotten into town after a long absence, and I was sitting in a chain restaurant called "Choices" having a cup of coffee. You've been there yourself—pink Formica-topped tables and padded gray vinyl chairs, neo-Asian designer food along with an assortment of muffins, croissants, "light" sandwiches, and weak coffee.

The place was deserted except for the Asian proprietor—he looked Korean—and the cook, a beefy blond girl in polyester slacks and running shoes who couldn't have been older than twenty-one or so. Choices wasn't a big hit in Akron, and neither was the mall it was in, which was also empty. You could almost hear the developer tearing out his hair and mumbling suicidal slogans like *underutilization*.

I'd ordered a muffin and coffee, and was staring out into the parking lot alternately wondering how to get back out of Akron and whether I should go ask the proprietor for some butter for the too-dry muffin. A late fifties Cadillac—a '59 model with those amazing twin ruby hooters for taillights—pulled into the parking lot. Two wild-haired blond kids got out of the front seat and after a moment's consultation headed into the deserted drugstore next to Choices.

Just as they moved beyond my line of vision one of the Cadillac's back doors eased open. A woman got out. Like the kids she

---

only the safety of her two children in return, and safe passage for herself to Attica. Enchanted by the beauty of the gown and diadem, the princess tries them on, and dies a horrible death as the two poisoned articles adhere to her flesh. In a futile attempt to remove the articles from his daughter's body, Creon likewise is killed. Medea, to complete her revenge, then kills her own children before Jason's eyes.

Now, that's a lot of blood and gore, just like Klein's story, but it is blood and gore with a difference. It is also loaded with practical wisdoms about how domestic and marital life is to be conducted,

SOME NOTES ON DETECTIVE METHODS

was wild-haired, but she was older, and her hair was jet black. She looked toward the drugstore her two companions had disappeared into, shook her head, then walked straight toward Choices. She seemed familiar, and after a moment I knew why.

Aside from tires, Akron, Ohio, is famous for just one thing. It has produced two of the most intelligent rock 'n' roll groups around. One of them is Devo, who used to wear flowerpots on their heads, quote obscure Russian sci-fi novelists, and hurl technonihilist imprecations. The other is Chrissie Hynde, the lead singer from the Pretenders. The woman heading for Choices was a dead ringer for Chrissie Hynde.

There are few people in the music world I'd rather meet than Chrissie Hynde. No one, actually. She's an angry woman with a first-rate mind, a singing voice like a cobra in a grease pit, and the diction of a machine gun with a trigger mechanism of pure Meth crystal. It's her anger that interests me most, because it's white-hot and sophisticated, the kind of fuck-you rage that no one is born with and only something deeper than private neurosis can transform. She's one of us who has seen her life and her city slowly disappear. She learned to use what was offered as replacement, but she hasn't been fooled by it.

I'm no *Rolling Stone* journalist, so when she pushed open the glass doors I merely sat in my chair and watched her. She sat

---

and about what happens when mistakes are made. On the whole, those wisdoms are still current, most of them so obvious there's no need to spell them out.

Klein is a dead end, so I can't let him guide you to anything more than a glimpse of the Reptile Machine. I can't change him, can't make him recognize his shallowness or the lethal consequences of his work. He makes good money, he gets to travel, and one of these days he probably will get a piece of the action.

From here, you'll be guided by Public Eye. He comes to you

41

42

down a couple of tables away and plopped a leather bag on the tabletop large enough to carry an electric guitar. I looked away.

Next thing I knew she was standing beside me. "You got a light, pal?" she asked.

I resisted the impulse to say "yes sir," and handed her a pink disposable light I'd swiped off a friend. She lit her cigarette and slipped the lighter into her jeans.

"You a local?" she demanded.

"Nope," I said. "Not anymore. I'm on a pilgrimage. I wanted to see how Akron has changed."

"What the hell for?"

"Akron is the dead center of North America, the heartland."

"You got the dead part right," she said, plunking herself down in the chair next to mine. She took a deep pull on her cigarette and blew a stream across the table. "But you're off base on the anatomy. If they gave the American heartland an enema, they'd stick it in at Akron."

I smiled but didn't say anything.

"You remember how this place used to be," she went on. "Lots of farms, people doing real work, having real lives. Not anymore. Now it's the fucking Inner Station."

"Of what?"

with a location, Akron, Ohio, with a strange personal history, and with a mission. Like me, he's after the parent of the Reptile Machine—the propellant agency of the Global Village. He's called it the Akron Design Center.

The Akron Design Center is much harder to locate than the city of Akron. It has no address, no payroll, nothing of the tangible elements of a normal research or public administration agency. Its strength and influence lie in the absence of directly manufactured products. Instead of fabricating goods, the Center spreads influence. It doesn't have employees, only a network of partly con-

SOME NOTES ON DETECTIVE METHODS

Her eyes narrowed slightly, as if there was a difficulty in thinking—and maybe in remembering. Most women are attractive when they're happy, but this woman became *very* attractive as her unhappiness became visible, lurid synaptic arcs of rage. Just like her music.

"If you listen, you can hear a weird hum around here," she said. "But when you look for it, there's nothing to see except franchise shit and industrial debris. So you decide that you're crazy, and maybe you go stare into a pool like Narcissus did. But when you do, all you see is the skeleton of a fish floating up to the surface. Do you know what I'm talking about?"

I shrugged. Curious talk for a place called "Choices" in an Akron shopping mall. "Are you who I think you are?" I countered.

She stubbed the cigarette out and lit another. "Yeah, sure," she answered distractedly. "No. I'm her twin sister. I'm nobody." The anger flashed more brightly in her eyes. "None of that shit matters. So don't push it."

"Push what?"

"Look, buddy. You're a man. I'm a woman. We're both reasonably smart, and attractive. Is that what you want? Go somewhere? Like, rent a motel room and get it on? Figure out a way to make a million dollars?"

---

scious agents whose actions are guided by subliminals emanating from the Center. I know this sounds crazy, but bear with us.

The Center, you see, operates in a way that is similar to computer operating shells. While a shell does not directly dictate activities within its subsystems, it does impose a system logic and an operational route map. The system logic either reserves and then conventionalizes design decisions—from the most fundamental level right through to primary concepts—or it prevents specific decisions from being made.

The Akron designs—this epoch's conceptual models—were

"No," I said, "I don't."

Her eyes softened. "Neither do I. I mean, you're probably a nice guy and all. But that's what we're *supposed* to do. You know what I want to do? I want to be able to go home, have a couple of kids, treat people well, play some music, and forget about all this shit piling up around me. I want to live without having some turkey gluing my pages together all the time."

"I know what you're saying," I said carefully, "but no one gets to do that. The world we grew up in is gone. It's been redeveloped. Yours, mine, everyone's. Not made any better, just redeveloped. Made the same as every other place so we're never sure quite where we are. And all so a few slicko shits can wear Italian designer suits and drive Mercedes 450SLs."

She grabbed my wrist hard for a moment, then let it go. A gray sedan pulled up outside, and two neatly dressed men got out. The car pulled away and the men entered Choices. They gazed around for a moment, then sat down at a table within earshot of ours.

"You're in Akron," she said. "Did you know that this is where it all started? Where it all comes from? I'm not sure which, but it doesn't matter. You know what's wrong with our lives?"

"I've got a few ideas," I admitted. "Here we are, nice decent immigrant stock meant to work and build and grow and take

---

propagated by no easily identifiable source. They were carried forward into common practice on a rhetorical wave of enthusiasm for efficiency and cost-effectiveness. Who can object to that? you might ask, and trot out homilies about the bottom line, cost-to-consumer, and the inevitability of a world economy.

Okay. Let's stop right here. Have a closer look at those homilies. Tell me about efficiency and cost-to-consumer when design facilities, along with their payrolls and disposable incomes, are removed to megalopolitan locations, while production is shifted to

SOME NOTES ON DETECTIVE METHODS

pride in our families and what we know and what we build for ourselves."

"You make it sound as cornball as a Norman Rockwell paint-ing," she chided.

"Well, maybe it is. No apologies. After a decade of having television blow Colombian snow up our nostrils, everything that doesn't involve a quick rip-off and a foreign car looks corny. We've had to spend our whole lives fighting every change because we don't trust what's behind them, fighting a vague something or other most of us can't even put a name to."

She looked into my eyes and grabbed my wrist again. "We have to fight the fucking changes," she said. "They just make for more *things,* and more garbage, and more shit in the water and the soil. They're making all the good things disappear. They're still there, but we can't see them."

The conversation was getting spooky. Two more neatly dressed men entered Choices, this time wearing sunglasses. They conferred briefly with the first duo, removed their sunglasses, then took a different table.

"There's this place in Akron," she said, her voice softer now as she eyed the new arrivals. "This *thing.* I can't really say what it is or where. But it's here. And it's creating the fade-out."

"Fade-out?"

---

the Third World, where labor is cheap and environmental standards are minimal.

Describe the bottom line of a world economy so wasteful of human and natural resources it is going to exhaust the planet of materials—renewable or nonrenewable—within fifty years. Now go back to the bottom line and see what it is. Or better, wait that half century and have your grandchildren do it from a garbage dump that covers the planet.

But meanwhile, beware. If you're unfortunate enough to stum-

45

"That's the best term for it, yeah. A kind of dimming of the surface. Fade-out. You described it, so you must suspect. It's maybe just a feeling, or an instinct. Those guys. This mall." She gestured around her. "This place. Where do they come from?"

"Choices."

"Yeah. But they're fake choices, you dig? They're *Obligatory Opportunities*. An opportunity isn't the same thing as a choice, not when you're being compelled into exploiting it. Or tricked into it."

Two more suits entered. They nodded at the other four, and sat down at a table near the door. "I don't want to exploit anything," I added. "Sometimes there isn't any choice."

"Yeah, well, you're in a lot of trouble, then. You've got to rip the cover off these phony choices. Otherwise you're paralyzed."

I glanced beyond her out into the parking lot. The two wild-haired kids were ambling across the parking lot. They opened the car door, tossed in several bags, then stood with the doors open, arguing about something.

"What am I looking for, exactly?"

"Give it your own name," she snapped. "That's your affair. I've got my name. Just remember that we can't have a decent life without it being possible for everyone and everything. So look for the design that prevents that from happening."

---

ble onto a visible element of the Akron Design Center you'll find yourself ascribing all kinds of spectacular and often deranged physical and metaphysical configurations to it, just like Public Eye does.

The Center is an authority that has none of the conventional attributes or tangible resources we associate with authority. There's no convincing evidence, one way or the other, that it even exists, just as there's none that the world around you is being controlled or is totally out of control.

The moment you decide that it is being controlled you will be

SOME NOTES ON DETECTIVE METHODS

"There're your friends," I said. "They just got into the car."
"Oh yeah," she answered, disinterestedly, "them."

The Cadillac pulled out from between the parking stripes and headed directly for Choices, picking up speed as it neared.

"Are those kids going to ram this place?" I asked her.

"That's up to you," she replied calmly. "Stop kidding around. That Cadillac and those kids aren't the most lethal things here."

---

forced to the inevitable conclusion that the controlling authorities and their mechanisms are malevolent. If not, why is there so much misery when there is so much wealth? From that point, any search for structured evidence of malevolence rears only paranoia. And whatever you do find will identify you as a radical, or a malcontent, or a screwball. Out the door of any rational, profit-oriented establishment.

But if you propose to demonstrate that the world is out of control you will instantly be subjected to a flood of data to contradict your proposal. The President winks at you from the

47

AKRON DESIGN CENTER ANTIDOTES
Education

A healthy and just society devotes its essential energies and a large share of its resources to educating its citizens to understand the world around them and to make informed choices about it. When it doesn't, it is *by default* a society dedicated to the opposite goals: political and social oppression, the creation and maintenance of ignorance and the protection of unearned privilege.

If—as is universally sentimentalized—the chief resource for our collective future is our children, then let's start taking the little buggers seriously and give them resources at the point where they're most capable of developing a taste for learning.

a: The intent and bias of the education system will be altered,

i.) to focus primarily on general knowledge and on conceptual train ing. Nearly anyone can learn to run a machine in about a week, so the current mania for "technical training" is neither relevant nor efficient. With the continuing shift to robotics and button pushing, we need more people capable of understanding why machines are running, where they're running to, and what they're running over;

ii.) to reverse qualification criteria and wage scales for teachers. Henceforth, primary-school teachers will be drawn from the

---

television set, and vague assurances of competent control ooze over and around you. You are enticed to give your love and your loyalty to soft drinks or chemical detergents, the local super-market shrills at you that it has everything you could possibly want and a little bit more, and everywhere you look you're staring into the business end of a cornucopia of products that invite confidence and crush doubts. From that point, any search for structured evidence likewise rears only paranoia. If you speak, you will be identified as a radical, or a malcontent, even a

SOME NOTES ON DETECTIVE METHODS

education system's most gifted achievers, will receive the highest level of remuneration, and will be required in turn to acquire the greatest densities of general and expert knowledge (a ten-volume curriculum specification manual to follow).

b: Professional educational theory will be outlawed, with severe penalties to anyone caught manufacturing or trading in it. This will wipe out the entire middle-management apparatus that alternately bleeds our education system financially or drowns it in half-baked notions misappropriated from competent intellectual disciplines. It will also free up enough money to put an enormous number of teachers into overcrowded classrooms.

c: University faculty will draw the smallest wages, but will be compensated by reduction in classroom time. University tenure would be replaced by a universal system of three- or five-year nonrenewable contracts. This will improve several elements of current university teaching, research, and scholarship, which are now in a more or less total state of senile atrophy.

University level instructors and scholars will be compelled by this shifting and fermenting system to renew their private research and teaching bases frequently. This will cause them to address questions related to quality and timeliness of knowledge rather than (as now) to merely protect the right to rot behind the closed doors of petrified academic specialties and wood-paneled faculty offices.

Academics will pay for the privilege of leisurely study and research with reductions in domestic security and middle-class splen-

---

screwball. Out the door of any rational, profit-oriented establishment.

That's the setup. Where Barry Klein sees nothing malevolent in the world around him, Public Eye sees potential or actual malevolence everywhere. He claims to have seen the machinery become visible, and plans to tell you about it before he disappears—and you and I with him.

It isn't very promising, is it? The victims are present, but the

dor, both of which are proven enemies of truth seeking and academic innovation. Academics will be forced by the changes to concentrate on improving teaching skills or on the vigorous pursuit of knowledge, not (as is now generally the case) on gaining tenure, high salaries, mortgages, pensions, medical and dental plans, and other niceties that have nothing to do with dedicated scholarship, good teaching, academic freedom, or the general well-being of advanced education.

Academics will also be encouraged to pursue outside activities related to their field. Notwithstanding, in negotiating new employment agreements, applied research and consulting will be given no more than equal weight to obtuse scholarly or research pursuits (for which greatly increased funding will be appropriated).

d: Such educational renovations will make education socially prestigious once more, and skilled educators and scholars will become our new role-models and social superstars. To keep egos in line, our universities will institute a supplementary funding program involving the sale of advertising on university faculty. For the price of a reasonable endowment, advertisers will be able to purchase space on the clothing of teaching and research professors. How about a large crest across the back of the tweed jacket and a smaller logo on the breast pocket, to be worn at all times during on-campus duty? Some examples: the Burger King Professor of Seventeenth Century Literature, or more politically revealing, The Gulf + Western Professor of Ecology, or the AT&T Professor of Creative Mathematics.

---

exact nature of the victimization and the crime is opaque, and the villain is totally elusive. Public Eye can't even name specific villains. How can he, when they may have no corporeal or otherwise assignable existence?

He'll find it difficult to hold a stable linear narrative together. The structure of the dramatic elements keeps being altered as he attempts to open his case. That doesn't bother him, because he has his own misgivings about the veracity of conventionally linear sequences. But at every turn he's invited to overvalue his personal lineage and history. Similarly, his inherited intellectual and moral

SOME NOTES ON DETECTIVE METHODS

RILKE'S DOG

Seated at a heavy oak table on the second floor of a modest château just outside the small Swiss village of Sierre in the Rhone Valley, an elderly man looks out the window, carefully adjusts the position of a vase filled with late and oddly discolored roses, and begins to pen a letter to a younger friend. It is mid-November, 1925.

For this man, who is the German poet Rainer Maria Rilke and my grandfather, letter writing is only partly the laconic communication of news. It is also the occasion for calligraphy, and at times poetry itself. He devotes the same intense energies to correspondence that he does—or did—to his poetry and to his frequently absent muse. But these are things readers can easily find out for themselves. What follows, however, only I can tell you.

As he inscribes the words across the page, Rilke pauses frequently to gaze out the window at a familiar sight. Across the

---

structures are undermined by invitations to action, by debris from induced appetites for violent solutions. Finally, there are no logically traceable clues to the malevolent authority he's pursuing, and there are no ascribable massacres and few murders to add dramatic élan. How will he trick his way through such a morass?

He has two things going for him. He's in the same world we're all in, and he has my authorial convictions about the necessity of his search.

I don't like what I see out there, either. The world I have to work with—at once one of the quieter corners of North America and

empty fields a small brown dog advances toward the poet's house, a small brown dog that to him is of vast and wholly secret importance. Rilke has slightly more than a year to live, and while he does not know the exact hour of his death, he is subtly aware of death's progress within his body. Recently, he's been sorting the accomplishments of his life, the successes and failures, recounting the moments of intense pleasure. His poetic labors are over, and have been for several years. His gaze, to use his own expression, no longer runs ahead of him like a dog. Now it is firmly fixed on the substantial and near, focusing his extraordinary faculties in an attempt to see things as they are.

Hence, situationally, the importance of the small brown dog that trots across the fields each day to visit his garden. Since the summer of 1921 the dog has made these daily visits, and dog and visit have become a measuring device for the poet, a decipherment that he has accepted—first reluctantly, now gratefully, but always secretly.

The reluctance derives from the dog's ostensible mission, which is, putting it crudely, to piss upon the poet's rosebushes and vines. This it accomplishes relentlessly at each visit, after which, eschewing both friendship or insults, it returns to its origins on its own mysterious schedule.

At first, Rilke was affronted and enraged at these desecrations,

---

the technological heart of the Global Village—is hardly a paradigm of what I'd call social harmony and happiness. Sure, there's material abundance and a reasonable liberty of action. But the victims are everywhere I look, identifiable by bursts of frenetic physical activity such as shopping, looking for entrepreneurial opportunities, or performing pleasureless exercises—aerobics or jogging. These bursts of activity are usually interspersed with periods of equally profound mental inactivity—alpha'd out in front of television sets.

That's *my* chief clue, of course: something is trying to prevent a

SOME NOTES ON DETECTIVE METHODS

throwing stones and hurling imprecations at the beast. But nothing stopped the dog, which, if thwarted initially, would retreat to the fields to sit on its haunches just out of reach until the poet's attentions wavered sufficiently to allow it to complete its mission.

Always one to attend to rituals and omens, the poet eventually became fascinated with the dog and with the cunning and tenacity with which it carried out its ritual mission. As if deferring to an angelic presence, the poet retreated before the dog's superior will. The visits thus became both clock and ceremony, and eventually the cipher to the poet's foreshortening vision, another of life's ironic pleasures.

Over the years, Rilke spent many hours pondering the dog. He imagined its genealogy, its homelife, its future—all of it fabricated, because he asked no one about the dog or its owner, and the dog appeared and disappeared out of apparent ether, giving no clues to either its origins or its eventual destination.

The dog simply *was*, and because of that, it became a part of Rilke's life and imagination. Yet attempts to penetrate the dog's imagination met with futility. What did *it* think it was doing, and why? Why a gloriously blooming vine rose one day and a barren bush rose variety another? The dog offered no clues. There was no pattern to the unhesitating daily choices of this messenger. Indeed, there seemed to be no exact message.

---

full-density narrative. I'm not surprised. An authority apparatus that claims to communicate all information and to tell all stories is one that is dedicated to the destruction of narrative and hostile to analysis. Its goal must be an absolute opaquing of perceived reality. Only that way can its violence be masked, transformed into a virus that undermines distinction and replaces it with a devouring inner hunger.

If you're not sure what I'm talking about, ask yourself how long it has been since you heard a fundamental question asked in public. Try these ones: *What are we doing here? What is human*

As his death approached, Rilke abandoned such speculations, shifting his focus to the dog as a physical presence. Here was an organized system operating within rational pathways designated by a binary logic without reflexive consciousness—feedback in its purest form, with no data loops or interventions for creativity to breed in.

I interrupt here, of course. That is my ironic description, the jargon of cybernetics that I, Rainer Maria Rilke's grandson, have playfully imposed in order to shock you. My grandfather's final intelligence saw the dog through a different economy: canine muscles rippling beneath the pocked brown fur, the lips lifting from the incisors in the parody of a human grin as the right hind leg lifted and the dog let go the jets of yellow urine, the ever-alert eyes scanning each shallow horizon for danger.

My grandfather spent his last years enjoined by this dog's being, and, imagining it for itself alone, he rejoiced in his heart at the strange gifts it brought him. And as we know from other records, he also despaired that such angelic presences were disappearing.

Me? Well, let me give you a brief genealogy and no more. My grandmother, an adventurous young woman and an admirer of the poet, appeared in his life briefly during the early part of

---

life for? Why doesn't our wealth make us kinder, more humane, and happier?

Because Public Eye and I have no stake in preserving the professional sanctities of our respective trades, we will be operating without the preconceived paradigms that subvert those questions—no predetermined answers. Nothing mysterious about that. But the disappearance of the world does involve a mystery, a horrifying, consuming mystery that may be masking a future worse than the Armageddon of the millenarians. That's the case we're on.

SOME NOTES ON DETECTIVE METHODS

February 1922. She took a room in the village of Sierre, and on a crisp, moonlit night set out shortly after nine P.M. for Rilke's château.

Over the next three weeks she visited him eight times, always at night. Her diary, which I was allowed to read just once when I was a boy, discreetly gave no details, save the exceptional note that she and the poet never once spoke directly to one another—possibly because my grandmother wished to hide her vulgar origins.

The visits ended on the ninth evening, when my grandmother found her way barred by a small, brown, snarling dog. A tenth attempt misfired for the same reason, after which she concluded that her adventure was over. She returned, without chagrin, to Paris. Six weeks later, realizing she was pregnant, she returned to the United States.

Her wealthy family in Boston, decidedly not liberal or adventurous, promptly disowned her. But my grandmother's fuel tank was not yet empty. She joined the Ringling Brothers circus, and spent five more months traveling with it, working the midway and performing a variety of unspecified services for the performers until it closed for the season in Cleveland. From there she went to Akron, Ohio, where she settled into a somber identity as a young but widowed mother. A few years later she came

---

WHAT BARRY KLEIN MISSES

Back in that first story, Klein refers to the Kincaid murders as a "tragedy," as if the term had common coinage. Maybe it does. But it's a degraded coinage: for him, a tragedy is merely a technical device—some bad news sensational enough to trigger the reptilian core of the human brain.

Tragedy once had a much more exact meaning, and it still has a

into some money, bought a rooming house, and lived out her youth as a den mother for factory workers from the city's automotive tire plants. My mother was born in Akron in December 1922, a love child who remained an only, and much beloved, child of the smoky Ohio hinterlands.

My mother inherited—or learned—the obscure but powerful passions of my grandmother. In her early twenties, while walking through a wartime railway station, she fell in love with a soldier. She plucked this man unerringly and on first sight, from a troop train headed overseas but temporarily stalled in Akron due to some mechanical problem with the locomotive.

The soldier, my father, promptly went AWOL for her, stayed a week with her in a dingy hotel room, then disappeared forever. My mother claims to this day that she neither knew nor asked his name, and that her passion was for his laughter, which she said bubbled confidently from him like water from a bottomless spring. The only other thing she told me about him was that he talked incessantly and at a very rapid clip. Maybe she never got to ask his name.

I was born from their union in the spring of 1945. And about me and my life there is little that you need to know, except that I am the unremarkable product of my native environment, my genetic antecedents, the solicitude of a loving grandmother and

---

profound history and pedigree. In the loosest sense it involves ironic struggle with evil: mistakes in perception are made, something bad happens, someone—those confronted directly or indirectly—learns from it.

Aristotle's discussion of tragedy in The Poetics reveals a still more interesting and complex process. For the Greeks, tragedy was much more than a simple dramatic relationship between protagonist and action. Their tragedies always had observers, both inside the play and outside. Public education had foremost importance.

WHAT BARRY KLEIN MISSES

mother, and of the swirling currents of dread, disappearance, and wasted wealth that characterize my generation. I am wholly human.

The foregoing may or may not have happened as I've described it. Certainly there is more to the story than I've revealed or know, but we're going to have to live with that. The mystery I'm here to unravel is not an autobiographical one. It concerns the world you and I inhabit together, and you should be undistracted by my identity.

Instead, sharpen your attentions on this anecdote, which contains far deeper and more important mysteries than those usually offered by private history or fiction:

Just a few weeks ago, I was staying in a hotel in a moderately large and cosmopolitan eastern city. In between appointments, I stopped into the hotel restaurant for lunch. I read through the menu and, because I'm an experienced traveler, ordered a club sandwich. Even in a bad restaurant a club sandwich is always edible. Ordering one is a way of finding out, with minimal risk, if a restaurant is any good. In a good restaurant the bacon will be crisp, and the chicken won't be machine-sliced. The french fries will tell you how vegetables are treated.

The waiter brought the club, placed it in front of me, and

By acting out *hubris* (unwarranted personal pride and error) in the face of physical world realities, the tragic protagonist is caught in a series of merciless structures that are also embodiments of abstractions: *nemesis,* at once retributive justice and the goddess of measure, appears. Her job is to provide the measure of human and cosmic damage inflicted and suffered, and her judgment invokes, for the protagonist, personal *catastrophe*—a term we're all familiar with, sort of, because it generally involves blood and gore.

But the most important element in the tragic formula for the

asked if I required any condiments—mentioning ketchup and, I think, HP Sauce. Taken off guard, I felt compelled to choose one of the two. I hesitated, then asked for ketchup.

"I probably won't use any," I added, "but having it on the table will make me feel more comfortable."

The waiter grinned, and as he wandered away in the direction of the kitchen I heard him chuckling.

A moment later he was back with a small porcelain jug, grinning, if anything, more broadly than when he left. He placed the jug on the table and showed me that it was empty. He explained that he'd tried to fill it with ketchup, but that someone had mistakenly put the ketchup in the freezer, and he'd been unable to remove any from the frozen container.

"I hope you don't mind, sir," he said, "but since you don't actually intend to use any ketchup, how about if you just *pretend* there's ketchup in the jug?"

"No problem," I said, delighted at the unexpected extension of the game I'd started.

I ate my club. It was edible, though it wouldn't win any culinary awards. When I finished I signaled to the waiter for the bill. He appeared moments later with a saucer that contained the bill and three wrapped mints.

As he slipped the saucer in front of me he grinned slyly.

Greeks was *catharsis,* which is a complex instrument of cultural regulation contemporary civilization has lost sight of. Probably that began when the word itself was mistranslated—or under-translated—as meaning merely "purgation," the purification or getting rid of guilt, remorse, and other waste products of living. Fully translated, *catharsis* means cleansing recognition that leads to revelation and the turning of thought and action—not garbage disposal. And it is a public as well as a psychological activity.

Tragedy isn't something that can happen within the privacy of consciousness—to an actor in a play or to an individual running

WHAT BARRY KLEIN MISSES

"And how was your ketchup, sir?" he asked.

"Oh," I said, "just fine. Exactly what was needed."

Now, the purpose of telling you this little anecdote is not merely to demonstrate what a witty guy I am. Far from it. The exchange between the waiter and me was an utterly unremarkable instance of shared laughter, the sort that takes place numerous times every day.

At closer scrutiny, however, it involved intellectual processes that are unique to human beings, and which any computer invented—or likely to be invented in the foreseeable future— would incinerate its circuits attempting to duplicate. In addition, the anecdote reveals a flaw in my grandfather's assessment of the small brown dog's mission. He was right about nearly everything else concerning the dog—the color and texture of its fur, its traverse of the fields, its general demeanor and tenacity, and about the importance he came to associate with it, right down to placement of the faded bouquet of discolored roses on his desk. But about the singular logic of its mission, he erred. He was given the dark angel of *our* world, and, without the equipment to penetrate its mystery, he mistook part of its implications.

The intellectual processes my friendly waiter and I used, and which the brown dog did not use, involve contextualization,

---

afoul of significant world realities in daily life. A tragedy must be witnessed. It involves an educational relationship between the person who acts and those who witness the actions. It is an extensive social activity. The protagonist suffers the consequences, the witnesses learn about world realities and how to deal with them. If the world realities aren't recognized, there's no extension, and no tragedy.

Tragedy involves an integrated concept of individual and world reality—*no man is an island,* and so forth. That's interesting, and so is the fact that there's no concept of mercy in tragedy, and thus

immensely intricate and obtuse contextualizations, as you will quickly recognize if you begin to take them apart. You will also, more than likely, understand roughly what they are. All humor involves extraordinarily complex contextualizations, ones that are unique to humans and inscrutable to binary computers.

Our ability to make those contextualizations is all that now stands in the way of the attempt by the Akron Design Center to disappear the human community.

---

no intermediary authority to free us from day-to-day responsibilities for our actions, collective or individual.

In the Medea of Euripides, for instance, Jason's abandonment of his wife and children to marry the daughter of a local king is brutally measured. Medea poisons the bride-to-be and her father, and then kills her own children. Jason himself later meets an ugly end. The audience is warned of the social consequences of betrayal, and of the political consequences of self-serving logic. But the private catastrophe of either Jason or Medea, which in our sense of tragedy has become the whole game, wasn't really all

WHAT BARRY KLEIN MISSES

AKRON DESIGN CENTER ANTIDOTES
The Arts

Squadrons of PUS draftees armed with custard pies will be assigned to monitor the Arts, with instructions to attack the periodic outbreaks of arrogant, obscure, or otherwise silly behavior chronic within the artistic community with appropriate weapons.

a: All visual artists must pass yearly examinations which would contain the following questions:
   i.) Explain the subject matter of four famous works of art.
   ii.) Explain the subject matter of the artist's last four works.
   iii.) Provide a definition of "form."

(Note: All questions must be answered without using the words "emotion," "feeling," or "universality.")

b: No musician may release a recording without having had employment for six months in a symphony orchestra, professional choir, or chamber music ensemble or as a primary-school music teacher.

c: Writers of all kinds are instructed not to sell their asses or their souls, or, for that matter, to spend time examining themselves for evidence of same. Since propaganda is an immoral if not legally

---

that important. Euripides recognized that such cheap thrills were essentially frivolous. His Medea was a *protagonist,* a carrier of ideas and actions spacious enough for a civilization to inhabit.

Four hundred years later, when Ovid recounts the same tale, the process has changed profoundly. The cautionary social and political messages are played down, and Ovid is more interested in the emotional transformation of the characters and their neonized traceries. Like Euripides, he portrays the great hero of the Argonauts as a muddle-headed jerk, but the characterization of Medea is far more dramatic. He portrays her as a powerful and

61

criminal activity, paid affiliation with any organization, commercial, political, or religious, for the purposes of writing propaganda will be punished in unspecified, nonlethal but thoroughly unpleasant ways.
d: All artists will spend a one-month annual term in the PUS.

---

passionate woman who is transformed into both a domestic dove and a lunatic harpy by her love for Jason. His Medea is a *character*, with handholds meant for temporary visits, one of a thousand options for titillation.

A contemporary version of the tale could go in a number of directions. It could, as with the version Klein tells, miss every cathartic moment and become a series of barely related sensational episodes that will have us suspiciously eyeing our spouses and friends, or scouring the field for entrepreneurial opportunities and messages.

WHAT BARRY KLEIN MISSES

SOME SCENARIOS FOR THE MARGINALLY PARANOID

First, let me assign a date to these scenarios. It is November 13, 1925. For the superstitious, that just happens to be Friday the thirteenth. Nobody at the Akron Design Center, then or now, is superstitious, and neither am I. I mention it as a courtesy and as a fact—and, more manipulatively, as an oblique hook to tempt your curiosity and to warn of strange events to come. It raises an interesting question, doesn't it? What is the singular quality or quantity of any given day in the past (or the present), and how much of it is going to be visible until long afterward?

On that particular day in 1925, most people outside the Akron Design Center saw nothing unusual about it. Some were engaged in diverse but relatively normal activities—writing letters to friends or thinking about the things that were particular and beloved to them. Of course, most of the people in the world on

---

Alternatively, our Jason might recognize the emotional insta-bilities of his Medea and seek professional counseling for her. A host of drug-dispensing functionaries would descend on the situation, and Medea would land up immobilized in front of her television set, bombed into paralysis by daily doses of chlor-promazine. When Jason's poor record was ferreted out, the children might be temporarily placed in foster homes. This would free Jason to "go for the gold" with his partners, and from there, if things went badly, the action would shift to a purely legal arena, with a battery of land-claim lawyers contesting the constitutional

64

that date were doing what most people are doing right now—
wondering where the next meal is going to come from. But before
I ask why that is the case—which I will—we need to widen the
field so we've got something substantial on which to construct the
scenarios.

As I said, it's November 13, 1925. What did happen that day?
In the newspapers, syndicated newspaper columnist Arthur
Brisbane was discussing the current controversy over the virtues
of euthanasia—without voicing any clear opinion of his own. But
he did have a few thoughts on the subject of labor and economics:
"The value of all things," he wrote, "depends on the value of
human labor. While labor goes up, other values must go up." (If
you replace the word "value" with "cost" it updates the maxim a
full half-century.)

In Paris, France, a homeless woman died of exposure after an
unseasonal snowstorm. In New York City, a man named
Nicholas Oper got drunk and stole a locomotive. For fairly obvious reasons, Oper had trouble hiding the locomotive once he
had stolen it, and even more trouble explaining himself when he
eventually sobered up. In Medford, Oregon, a young man who
was to be married instead inexplicably shot his fiancée dead with
a .38-caliber revolver and then killed himself. In Brockville,
Ontario, a Canadian Pacific Railway ticket-taker locked himself

---

contraction of the contending parties. This is a less violent tale
than Klein's, but no more satisfactory. Nobody will learn a
damned thing from it, and the human wreckage and environmental debris will continue to pile up around us, even if our gloriously
inefficient systems of social adjustment managed to do their job
successfully.

Tragedy is an instrument worth exhuming, not because we can
easily pick it up and start using it again, but because it might tell
us what is lacking in our societies, and in our conceptions of
polity and public education. It is the antithesis of media-

WHAT BARRY KLEIN MISSES

in the station washroom and blew his brains out with the same caliber gun. There was a train wreck in Plainsboro, New Jersey.

Off the Devonshire coast in southwestern England, the British submarine *M1* inexplicably sank to the ocean floor with sixty-eight seamen on board. Various agencies were tentatively pointing fingers at one another, but the most reasonable explanation offered (as always) was human error.

In the Far East, Japanese warships sailed on Tsingtao, China, "in order," the official military communiqué read, "to protect the security of Japanese nationals and their assets." In Egypt, British archaeologists discovered and instantly violated the tomb of a young pharaoh named Tutankhamen.

In a New Jersey chicken coop, a very short man removed the shutters from a glassless window and gazed out across a frosted field. A beautiful young woman carrying a young child was advancing across the field toward him. Not far from the chicken coop and the gore of the Plainsboro train wreck, little Herman Kahn in Bayonne, New Jersey, only a few months older than my mother, was arranging groups of tin soldiers on the patterned carpet of his parents' living room, mimicking what he imagined were the sounds of dropping bombs and removing the groups of soldiers one after another, plick, plack, plonk.

---

structured reality—the output of the Reptile Machine. In a tragedy, individual life and purpose are measured by societal and natural forces. Not the other way around, as in Klein's view.

There's only one thing wrong with tragedy. The social and ecological structure of our world is too fragile to bear the consequences of our vast hubris. Retributive justice for our globally scaled fuckups would mean an end to the audience.

In an inspired piece of scholarship published nearly thirty years ago, American poet Louis Zukofsky made a convincing argument

Seated at a heavy oak table on the second floor of a modest château just outside the small town of Sierre in the Rhone Valley, an elderly man looks out the window, adjusts the position of a vase of oddly stained roses, and begins to pen a letter to a younger friend. A small brown dog trots toward him across a field.

Governments all over the world were proposing direct taxes on business activities for the first time, and most business leaders were crying foul and running ten feet in one direction, then ten feet in the other. Some of them, however, were doing something about it.

I haven't brought all these data into a single field just to remind you of how full with events and things the world is at any given moment, nor have I done it to be able to make the cynical observation that most of them are either repetitive or irrelevant.

No, I am here to propose that every trail in our mystery can be tracked backward to this remarkable—and unremarkable—day in 1925, and to develop the alternate scenarios about those events that will allow you to see what is at risk here.

Imagine the first think tank held by the Akron Design Center. It took place before most of us were born, and it was clandestine in a way we can't imagine. Nothing of it was recorded—Richard Nixon and Rose Mary Woods hadn't yet been invented. So I've

---

that all dramatic action in Shakespeare's plays originates in defects of vision—people failing to recognize their own identities and situations accurately, failing to recognize those of the people around them, or failing to note the true nature of the environments in which they are operating. In Shakespeare's comedies, the defects of vision are correctable, and are corrected in the course of the action—a catharsis of folly by folly. In his tragedies, the defects of vision might well be correctable, but they aren't corrected. As a consequence kingdoms fall, and people die or are reduced to abject misery.

WHAT BARRY KLEIN MISSES

had to imagine what went on. I've set the event, on the basis of some fairly reliable research, on the morning of November 13, 1925.

Think tanks have been a respected Western planning device since the Great War of 1914–1918. Competent professionals and experts are brought together in an institution to think through specific subject areas, or issues. Most major industries now have them, and more than a few governments rely heavily on them in determining policy and programs. They're an integral part of our way of life.

But how effective are they, and what is it they really do? After seventy years of think tanking, people all over the world are wondering where their next meals are coming from, and no think tank has ever seriously addressed the problem. They just can't be set up to deal with such multiple-variable problems.

Doesn't it make you wonder just a little? That an overwhelming proportion of humanity still expends the greatest portion of their energies worrying about their next meal is probably the chief failure of the human community. Arguably, a *greater proportion* is now fixed on that question than fifty or a hundred years ago.

Before we go any further along this depressing track, stop and think about just what a think tank is, what it is set up to

---

Zukofsky made no claims for dramatists other than Shakespeare, but I'd be prepared to argue that Zukofsky's principle is the essential structure in all comedy and tragedy, which are now the only literary forms that have not been undermined by the discoveries of modern science, or the less certain paradigms and pragmatic disciplines of contemporary psychology. I'd also be prepared to argue that accuracy of recognition, and/or the failure to make fundamental recognitions is the source of all public and private disorder.

Outside comedy and tragedy, of course, resides the rest of

accomplish, and which intellectual procedures it has supplanted.

First, all think tanks operate from defined and generally quite narrow terms of reference—they create or re-create reality without discussing their fundamental assumptions about it. By definition, then, a think tank is a binary instrument dedicated to generating strategies that are based on assumptions deliberately placed beyond the field of focus. The Akron Design Center assumptions are roughly as follows:

1. *Maintenance of Western-style capital accumulations is the primary good, and must be protected.*
2. *The poor peoples and nations of the world are opportunities for near-term exploitation and control, or reserves for future development.*
3. *The redistribution of wealth, where it occurs, must not threaten the current holders of wealth and privilege.*
4. *Loyalties to geopolitical class and to corporate solidarity supersede loyalties to nation or to moral concepts and ideas. Corporate "morality" will be successful to the extent that it avoids questions of universal value and individual conduct and concentrates on purely situational ethics aimed at protecting corporate viability and/or profits.*

Before you accuse me—and this—of cynicism, let me turn that charge squarely at the think-tank mentality. Cynicism, whatever

---

public theater, along with most of the rest of narrative thinking. Despite its many innovative virtues, very little of it now contains values—formal or moral values—that consciously account for the impact of modern science and communications technologies. Most of it now operates toward the same cultural values and impacts those tourist-targeted "pioneer" villages seek to achieve. In those, people carry out obsolete and generally time-wasting, laborious practices for the amusement of gawking tourists. I'm not sure what most literary writers think they're doing these days, but it's evident that they don't think about it very often beyond

WHAT BARRY KLEIN MISSES

finery it is dressed up with, is a capitulation to things as they are. It is diametrically opposed to my impulse, which is carefully ironic. Irony begins with the attempt to see things as they really are, but reserves a part of the imagination for the kind of world we might have—or, more accurately, could and should have.

I can't, of course, certify the assumptive base of the Akron Design Center via the rules of legal proof. Such a project would take decades of research, with a staff of hundreds and a research budget in the millions. I'd love to direct such a project, but I'm not holding my breath while I wait for someone to make me the offer. Meanwhile, I'm using imaginative supposition—that is, fiction—which allows me to say "looking at the past sixty years, what would a 1925 think tank have assumed in order to create this world?"

Admittedly, no think tank would try to imagine a world sixty years hence. But at the root of every think tank is a fantasy about the future, an invisible, venal Utopia of pure self-interest.

The Akron Design Center think-tank assumptions weren't simply responding to a vision of the future. That was part of it, sure, but it was also addressing a tangible phenomenon. The phenomenon was that of astounding increases in productivity brought about by the technological discoveries that had flooded the world in the first two decades of the century. The vision was

questions of how to milk the traditional machinery of literature for maximum effect. It's also evident—by the sheer numbers of university professors who make their living interpreting literary works—that the primary intellectual interest and energy since the 1940s have been curatorial.

Despite formal experiments and the abundance of ostentatious ambition, there's little in the worldview of writers today that touches the realm of tragedy, and there's progressively less that writers render as true comedy. Both require a participating public audience, and literature rarely commands that nowadays. Maybe

that the human community was about to be deluged by an outpouring of material wealth.

Nor was the Akron Design Center alone in spotting what was about to happen. Until the Great War, Western governments hadn't done much except charge import taxes, collect user tolls on a variety of services and public assets, and organize citizens to kill and loot people in the poor countries of the world. The Great War exacted an unprecedented cost in human lives. It was also extremely expensive, and the war debts had to be paid. A tax on citizens' incomes had already been created, but it wasn't producing enough revenue because workers were much poorer in those days than now. These same governments were also getting funny notions about taking care of the war casualties, and about generally improving the lot of the common people, and generally fantasizing about distributing the oncoming wealth.

There was also a perceived global threat, perhaps the first that could be regarded as an organized threat. Bolsheviks had taken control of Russia, and Marxists around the world were still confidently predicting that the rest of the industrialized nations would soon capitulate to their dictatorship of the proletariat. In the Marxist fantasy, capitalism was supposed to have collapsed immediately after the Great War, but it hadn't. Undeterred as always by pragmatic reality, Marxist theoreticians were still

---

that's what has that raw nerve jangling: What becomes of writers who can imagine no other world than the one they're in?

Literary writing has become a professional or academic activity, which is to say, it now carries a covert collusion with the status quo into the realm of phenomena. Sometimes the collusion is a Volvo wagon, a driveway, or ballet lessons for the children, and sometimes it's the grinning arrogance of a Marie Antoinette.

The mutant technologies of neonarrative—consumer advertising, motivational and marketing research, and the professional pollsters—have usurped (and vastly enlarged) the audience for

noisily plotting a world uprising. Meanwhile, workers everywhere, sensing the increase in general wealth, were starting to
wake up to the strange idea that it wasn't part of a natural,
eternal order that they be treated as animals. This was interpreted as evidence of a genuine Communist threat. It was these
factors—these contending fantasies about how to distribute the
outburst of material wealth—that spurred the Akron Design
Center think tank.

Let's flesh out the stage sets a bit, television-movie style. The
first Akron Design Center think tank meets in the modestly
appointed boardroom of a large, unnamed company in Akron,
Ohio. Outside the window, a steel-gray sky perfectly reflects the
eyes of the man at the head of the table. He is in his late fifties,
slightly overweight, and he wears his double-breasted navy pin-
striped business suit as if he's been born in it. Despite his
advancing years, his jaw is resolute, his manner crisply authoritative as he arises from an oxblood leather padded chair. He
surveys the room gravely, lifts a small ebony gavel above the table's
surface, and taps lightly to get the attention of the other nine
similarly dressed men around the table. Eat your heart out,
James Clavell.

SPEAKER #1: Gentlemen. It is time to organize ourselves. There

---

fictional narrative. They've given the visible elements over to
television, to sensationalist novels, and other purely consumer
media. This has left literature as a profession without a publicly
valued purpose or much of an audience. It has also imprisoned us
all in a complex of motivational contraptions that puke out a vast
array of consumer products and social control apparatuses. Local
and natural narrative is replaced by system demands and market
logic.

Public Eye has any number of inappropriate responses to the
professionalized degradation of literature. The one that interests

71

are historic opportunities opening for men like us. If we do not grasp them firmly, they will elude us. They are opportunities of the widest possible implication. We can alter the community and economy of nations. We can secure for ourselves and other like-minded individuals a place of wealth and privilege for generations to come.

SPEAKER #2: Henry Ford has said that the best way to achieve progress and to keep the Bolsheviks at bay is to place heretofore undreamed-of quantities of mass-produced goods into the hands of citizens. The way to greater wealth is to use our new production techniques to create and distribute commodities to those capable of laboring to earn them. Material poverty is the seedbed of seditious ideas. We will sterilize that seedbed with goods carefully designed to addict and render impotent the majority of citizens.

SPEAKER #3: Such a program requires careful design if it is to succeed. The accumulations of low-level wealth must not build up too quickly. If they do, citizens will begin to examine the quality of life the wealth brings, and our strategy may become transparent.

SPEAKER #4: I suggest that we allow the economy to continue in its present course for no more than five years, and then force an artificial collapse. The influx of commodities will head off the

---

me the most is laughter. There is no laughter in a logical process. When you get the giggles while you're drowning in a river it may be illogical, but there's something more distinctly human about it than those humorless aquatic technocrats doing laps from bank to bank, their muscled bodies greased like machines, their minds focused on fitness goals or on some private competition with numerical reality.

The function of laughter, according to MIT Media Lab founder Marvin Minsky, is to disrupt another person's reasoning and to

WHAT BARRY KLEIN MISSES

Bolsheviks in the near term, and the withdrawal of them will make the consuming classes extremely reactionary.

SPEAKER #5: A crash will be easy to engineer. We'll overheat the stock market and inflate the value of shares. Then we'll leap out together, remove our cash reserves to Switzerland, and then move back in to pick up the pieces when the market hits bottom. Our cash reserves will allow us to pick up massive land and production holdings very inexpensively. The result will be a consolidation of actual wealth, but with the appearance of massive losses. What losses do occur will clear residual inefficiencies and weaknesses. Housecleaning, as it were. Periodic massacres of small or overeager investors is a necessary adjunct to our general strategy.

SPEAKER #6: This apparent cataclysm will drain social and political energies for forty years—at least two generations, perhaps three, will be defined by it. The near-term crash will make the present generation and their children permanently hungry. We'll feed them with a steady flow of material goods and allow them to rebuild their wealth and confidence.

SPEAKER #7: To achieve this, however, we may need a major war. With the terms set by the Treaty of Versailles, the preconditions have been created for the temporary rise of right-wing nationalism, and for the further isolation of the Bolsheviks inside Russia.

---

focus attention on the present state of mind and its immediate environment. In the realm of logic, laughter is an instrument of disruption and system mayhem.

So, just for a break, let me sink beneath the currents and tell you some funny stories as I drift downstream. One of them even has a river in it.

1. A moose hunter stands on the bank of a small but fast-flowing river. He is clad in a tartan mackinaw and hipwaders, the former worn as protection against the chilly air, the latter as

After the war, the majority will be battle-shocked, and will want to consume more goods, just as they did after the Great War. We will reward citizen isolation and consumer conformity. Having defeated the political evils in the world, the postwar generation will be eager to forge a private share of the opportunities for wealth created by the reconstruction. Most will become addicted to the new surge of material goods. Others will become addicted to the pursuit of wealth itself. The few skeptics who stand outside this will be so effete that they'll lose all their energy trying to recognize that it isn't what they don't have that enslaves and impoverishes them, but what they *do* have.

SPEAKER #8: We must be invisible in all this. We will diversify our asset-holding and executive patterns—by creating larger corporate bodies, and by diversifying apparent control through interlocking directorships and opaque ownership patterns. Of course, some figurehead leaders will emerge for public consumption, but these will give every appearance of philanthropic concern, in the Carnegie model, or that of the Rockefellers. We will transform Woodrow Wilson's political internationalism into a more malleable economic internationalism. This will involve disguising our goals, and infiltrating state bureaucracies and legislative bodies with agents who will alter the tax and tariff structures in our favor.

---

defense against the boggy marsh the river is surrounded by. He is a serious hunter, as evidenced by the .475 Winchester rifle slung over his shoulder.

As he surveys the opposite bank, to his amazement a bull moose appears from the underbrush less than a hundred yards downstream. He swiftly unslings the rifle, lifts it to his shoulder, sights up on the moose's head, and pulls the trigger.

There is a visible puff slightly above the moose's skull, and the left side of the rack of antlers falls to the ground. The moose staggers, but remains standing, stunned by the combined impact

WHAT BARRY KLEIN MISSES

SPEAKER #9: We will quietly gain economic control over the press and in particular over the new radio and motion picture technologies. Once we control these, we will maintain the illusion of complete openness while preventing debate at any depth simply by breaking up discourse with advertising. Ultimately, our goal is to marry the two. Government regulatory bureaucracies will become very powerful, and will have to be undermined. In the near term this can be accomplished through direct influence and where necessary, violence. In the long term, we must break government's power by forcing it to adopt our models for economic planning and internal performance evaluation. High among the achievements of the Akron Design Center has been its ability to convince a large percentage of the industrialized and wealthy West to do this voluntarily.

A jump cut occurs here. The scene shifts to a white room overlit with hyperbrilliant cool-white fluorescents. The same characters are there, but now they sit around a sterile white table. Costumes have shifted from business suits to laboratory coats.
SPEAKER #1A: Gentlemen. It is time to organize ourselves, and so forth, on up to this exact moment, without interruption. And

---

of the rifle's .475 charge and the illegal hollow-bore slug the hunter was using.

The hunter doesn't get a second shot. The riverbank on which he's standing has been undermined by his weight and by the rifle's powerful recoil. Bank, hunter, and rifle unceremoniously collapse into the fast-moving currents of the river. The hunter's hipwaders fill with water and he is dragged beneath the surface. The moose is still standing motionless, staring dazedly at the swirling waters as the current takes the thrashing hunter past. The sight of a human being startles the moose from its empty reverie,

in case you've decided that I'm just kidding, do a little research of your own on these three organizations:

1. Council on Foreign Relations (United States, f. 1918): "It is a board of initiation—A Board of Invention. It plans to cooperate with the government and all existing international agencies, and to bring them all into constructive accord" (1919 CFR handbook). The CFR heavily influenced the formulation of NATO, the World Bank, the International Monetary Fund, and other elements of the Bretton Woods System (named after the Bretton Woods, New Hampshire, conference in 1944 that settled the structure of pre-Organization of Petroleum Exporting Countries [OPEC] geopolitical and economic reality). Still exists.
2. The Bilderberg Group (f. 1954): European-led anti-Communist group of business leaders which led to the formation of the Atlantic Alliance, strengthened NATO, and was instrumental in creating the European Economic Community (EEC). It stressed the link between domestic and international stability. Still exists.
3. Trilateral Commission (f. 1973): Created officially in 1973 by David Rockefeller, chairman of Chase Manhattan Bank, but energized by U.S. President Richard Nixon's August 15, 1971, announcement of the protectionist "New Economic Policy." Its appearance is simultaneous with the 1973 oil crisis. Originally it drew its two hundred members from the financial, political, diplomatic, and academic

---

and it crashes awkwardly and asymmetrically into the underbrush.

2. At the height of what was presumably an erotic dream a young man awakens in a darkened Akron, Ohio, apartment to discover what he thinks is a prowler in his bedroom. He reaches carefully behind his head, removes the .45-caliber automatic pistol he keeps beneath his pillow, and without hesitating, shoots the head off his erect penis.

3. A Louisiana family gets into a violent argument over some incidental point of domestic protocol. The family's elderly patri-

WHAT BARRY KLEIN MISSES

elite of Japan, Europe, and North America. Most recently created the conceptual blueprint for the Canada/U.S. Free Trade Agreement. Still exists.

Now, I have no absolute way of proving that the Akron Design Center think-tank session took place, or if such consciously organized strategies were decided upon. What I am saying is that if one were to make a regression analysis of the enacted strategies of Western business leaders, it would be quickly discovered that this scenario is as credible an illustrative fiction as are the conventional histories.

Still, I'd be the first to admit that my scenario has two basic weaknesses. One of them suffers from the same weakness all political paranoia has: however sound its conclusions are, paranoiac reasoning demands order and control as a precondition for order and control—be it divine, extraterrestrial, corrupt capitalist, or dialectics-crazed Marxist-Leninist in character. Political paranoids—in fact, all paranoids—are reactionaries first and finally.

The other weakness is one that I'm painfully aware of, having put you through the scenario. It's lousy drama. After all, what could be more boring than a business meeting? There's no passion, and no poetry. That being the case, let's see what I can find

---

arch, who suffers from kidney failure and is hooked up to a dialysis machine as the argument begins, quickly grows frustrated with his inability to control the situation, and pulls a revolver from a night table beside his bed. While he is waving it at them and demanding they stop, the revolver accidentally discharges. The family members stop arguing and scatter wildly. When they return to the room minutes later they discover that the ricocheting bullet has severed a tube on the dialysis machine. The patriarch has bled to death.

Now, these stories—they're really just anecdotes, I guess—are

78

in the other events of November 13, 1925, and see what I can weave them into.

But which event shall we choose, and toward what end? No doubt you've become aware of the slowly descending net of biographical hints, clues, and details concerning my identity and those of my immediate forefathers. So far, there is grandfather, grandmother, mother, but no father. Is my father lodged somewhere in the current skein of detail? Maybe, but I'm not going to tell you stories about myself unless I can substantiate them.

Since we're a society deeply fascinated with ordnance, let's begin there. The Medford, Oregon–Brockville, Ontario duo involves two identical guns and three shootings. Is this perhaps a love triangle? Did the fiancée of the male Medford protagonist pass through the Brockville, Ontario railway station, fall instantly and passionately in love with the ticket-taker, and did they dally carnally in a station washroom or office closet? Then, weeks later, on the prenuptial eve, was the bride overtaken with guilt and did she therefore confess—or declare her intentions of leaving for Brockville on the morning train? Or have we got the dalliance all wrong, and it was the bride-to-be who discovered a passionate letter from the Brockville ticket-taker to her fiancé, and threatened to tell all? Hmmm. . . .

---

funny in a very particular way. First, despite the ultimate consequences in all three, none involve tragedy. We all know guns are dangerous, but the arguments for and against their use are simplistic and partial. Yet the Zukofsky/Shakespeare paradigm pertains in all three. Each gun was loaded and fired by defects of vision.

The hunter should have used a smaller rifle, and probably should have fired at the body of the moose, preferably just behind the front shoulder so that the bullet would penetrate the animal's heart. But our man knew that the combined impact of the rifle's heavy caliber and the hollow-bore slugs he was using would

WHAT BARRY KLEIN MISSES

And what is it with all these trains? If we add Nicholas Oper to this brew it changes again. Perhaps Nicholas was a close friend of our Brockville ticket-taker, and had stolen the locomotive with the crack-brained plan of picking up his friend and speeding to Oregon to stop the wedding. Did he, on the way to Brockville, pass through the Plainsboro yard, and trip a switch that later caused the train wreck?

Was little Herman Kahn somehow involved? Was he, at the tender age of three, between episodes of pulling wings from flies and liquidating armies of tin soldiers, experimentally switching tracks? Were the Japanese involved, or did the opening of King Tut's grave incur a cosmic drift of tomb dust? Was the ticket-taker's older brother among the crew of *M1*? Where was Richard Nixon while this was going on? Is J. D. Salinger mysteriously responsible for any of this?

This is getting nowhere. Everything here is potentially connected, once the paranoiac expectation of order and control is delivered. So let me get to the nub of all this, to the true romantic scenario:

Right now the world feels like it must have felt to Rilke in 1925. Why? Nineteen twenty-five wasn't a bad year. Yes, but it had some deep and ugly currents starting to swirl just beneath the surface, and some uneasy players. My grandfather, near the end

---

render much of the meat inedible. His decision to shoot the moose in the head was stupid—and ironically lethal—but it was nonetheless an expert and perfectly logical decision. The logic simply didn't account for enough factors, or for the right factors.

The incident in the Akron apartment has similar but more psychologically complex characteristics. The problem is deciphering the nature of the error, and the exact lesson to be learned. Obviously, security-freaked males prone to nocturnal erections shouldn't sleep with handguns under their pillows. But

of his string, was one of them. If I run the tape ahead a few years from 1925, it's 1933, and Adolf Hitler has arrived in power, backed by big business and a horde of confused purity freaks. A few years more and the subterranean currents he opened are clogged with human corpses.

My questions are these: How much of that could have been glimpsed in 1925? Why didn't anybody stop it? Are we again at the beginning of a similar buildup of lethal authority?

Hindsight shows us that the events of 1925 were the warm-up acts to a fundamental alteration in human relations, one that mercifully turned out to be temporary. Today, there's evidence to suggest that we're again facing another fundamental alteration in human relations.

At this point we might cop out and propose the nihilist's scenario. Perhaps there is no order whatsoever, and life is a marvelously spinning contraption with absolutely no goal, an irrelevant parade of robbery opportunities and BMW dealerships.

Perhaps mercifully, we can prove the accuracy of none of these scenarios. We must therefore rely on the physical evidence of the world around us. Read the signs around you as I have done. And by all means, read on. From here on, though, the trail of the Akron Design Center will be tracked differently. I can't take you

---

that's too simple. If the man hadn't had an overabundance of male hormones, which provided both his aggression and his erection, do you think he'd have fired the gun? Did he, in fact, shoot the real prowler?

The fate of the Louisiana patriarch, similarly, has a deeply ironic message to deliver about the fragility of both authority and contemporary technology.

All three anecdotes are uncomfortably comic, deliciously ironic, and they do deliver a bizarre kind of catharsis of folly by folly. But the guns are still there, and we have to admit that the

WHAT BARRY KLEIN MISSES

through the front door because there is no front door. I will therefore take you to the moments of crisis, insight, and, curiously, comedy through which I and my coinvestigators have glimpsed the Akron Design Center. Sometimes you will see it coiling around the human figures like a corrosive cloud swirling around a stone angel. Other times, you will glimpse the comic human figures rising out of it like sweet music from the silence of a half-constructed tomb.

---

victims died without supportable causes. We're living in a world that spends almost a trillion dollars annually on weapons, but we're not quite in the realm of either tragedy or comedy.

Like tragedy, true comedy must have a public ritual attached to secure its cosmic ramifications. In comedy, however, when the defects of vision have been arrested in their course and been corrected, the participants—conceptual and human—are wedded, and wrongs are *seen* to be righted. A public feast—the Komos—then celebrates the triumph of humane wisdom and sensible diplomacy. Everyone is invited to the Komos, and

AKRON DESIGN CENTER ANTIDOTES
Economics, Stock Market Transactions, and Financial Speculation

a: Stock market and currency speculation are a major contributor to economic instability, and a source of unproductive wealth. They are quasi-criminal parasitic activities in which speculators bet on the productivity and economic luck of direct participants in the economy. Hence, existing stock exchanges would be closed, and the issuing, buying, and selling of stocks and bonds declared *semilegal*.

Stocks and bonds will be obtainable only in one or two dark alleys designated in the roughest section of each city. No police personnel or equipment would be allowed inside a two-block radius, even on report of a serious crime. All stock transactions will have to be in cash.

This will force investors to take real risks—only fair, since that's what they're constantly claiming they do. The benefits of this alteration of investment procedures could prove to be profoundly positive, resulting in greater economic stability and smaller-scale economic activities. It will also create new and ongoing mechanisms for redistributing wealth from the rich to the poor.

b: To keep our economic system from devouring its most productive elements (i.e., the smallest units):

---

you can bet your ass nobody begs off because he or she has an aerobics class or wants to go to a business seminar.

What I'm saying is that these days, we've lost the knack of correcting our systems, and that none of them are set up to correct themselves. There is no Komos for us to attend. Despite the enforced gaiety of our Disneyfied lives, deep down we know there's nothing worthy of a public celebration. Why do we agree to live under the stress of these compulsory festivals that celebrate only the power of the systems we're trapped in? Why aren't we looking for ways to regain control of those systems?

WHAT BARRY KLEIN MISSES

i.) A ten-year moratorium will be declared on corporate mergers, takeovers, and buyouts, and all corporate shareholders under the age of sixty would be required to hold active employment in the corporation or company, or be subject to six months' annual service in the PUS labor pool. To discourage interlocking directorships and market straddling, shareholders in more than one company would be subject to mandatory annual six-month PUS duty.

ii.) Newly franchised business operations would be strictly prohibited. Existing franchises will be subjected to a 10 percent civic tax on either sales or gross profits in order to replace the operating and development capital they bleed from local economies.

c: *In Search of Excellence* will continue to be sold, but it will be translated by a TIA panel and retitled *In Search of Profits* to more accurately reflect the true focus. All business, professional, and economic "self help" seminars will be attended by TIA panels armed with translation mandates.

THE CRIME, AND THE VICTIMS

For most of the last half of the twentieth century, what is humane and local has been disappearing.

That sounds too mystical even for me, so let me restate it in the language of contemporary science fiction:

Perception is being widely and profoundly manipulated and shaped in order to devalue and degrade the quality and variety of both individual and collective experience. Moreover, conscious-

THE ORGANIZER

There's a woman walking toward me across the scrappy asphalt of the parking lot. Her name is Candy Basalle, and she has her two-year-old daughter on her hip. The child is like her mother, dark curly hair, large brown eyes—a beauty, someday, if she's luckier than her mother.

Candy isn't beautiful. She's intelligent and tough, and that's more interesting. In her free hand is a sheaf of papers, and on her face is a familiar expression that manages to be unhappy and determined at the same time. She also has a black eye.

"I can't come to the meeting tonight," she says as I climb out of my battered Volkswagen. "My husband is back."

"That's too bad," I say, eyeing the shiner. "It would be good for you to be there. The others need you."

I don't ask her to elaborate. I'm pretty sure I already know the

---

ness is being artificially limited, and human mental processes are being restructured to conform with those of a nonhuman life-form.

This doesn't sound much like the generally accepted view of what's going on. We're living in the Age of Progress—the era of the Information Revolution—aren't we? If you watch television or read fashionable magazines and ignore events in the "under-developed" parts of the world, you'll get the impression that we're progressing. We'll soon be healthier, happier, better in-formed, and fully electronic—and richer than ever.

THE CRIME, AND THE VICTIMS

story. She'll say something about how her husband is away too much, and how he wants her to be around when he's there. She won't say what *she* wants, which is probably halfway between wanting to plant a hatchet in his forehead and simply to be elsewhere, away from the stained white plastic of Cottonwood Estates and away from men who beat on women.

I've heard that side of the story already. During the last three weeks I've spent five afternoons at her apartment with her and three of the other women in the complex. I've been listening to their complaints about the way they live, and trying to convince them they should take over the organization. The other three women are single parents. Candy is near the end of a bad marriage she got into when she was nineteen. She's twenty-four now, but she looks older. Especially with the shiner.

She repeats herself as she hands me the papers. "Well, my husband is back. You know. I gotta go back now. Hand these out, will you?"

"Oh, sure," I say, grinning at her sympathetically. The papers are the minutes of the last meeting.

She grins back and a blood bruise on her full lower lip becomes visible. "Catch ya," she says.

"Maybe next meeting you'll be free," I call out to her as she picks her way between the parked cars. I leave the multiple

---

Look again. More than twenty years have passed since Marshall McLuhan made it fashionable to think that what is occurring is an electronically aided return to tribal consciousness. He predicted an information-driven return to collective consciousness in which a tech-aided fine-tuning of systems would enrich and democratize public and private existence while ensuring the survival of the species and most other forms of organic life on the planet.

We don't seem to be heading in any particular direction at all these days. We're merely going faster and faster. Our lives are

meanings wide open for her to interpret. Not one of them is personal.

Tonight is the second meeting the Cypress Neighborhood Improvement Association has held at Cottonwood Estates. The first meeting was held in Candy's apartment. Ten people were there. About all they were able to fix on during that meeting was a name for the organization, which they took, rather cunningly, from the adjoining complex, Cypress Estates. Cypress Estates is a little smaller and older than Cottonwood Estates, and if anything, a little worse.

"That's what everyone calls the neighborhood," Candy explained when I asked why they were naming the organization after another apartment complex. "I guess the name stuck after they built Cottonwood Estates because Cypress rhymes with 'depressed.' It'll help us get members from over there, too."

Or, I thought, the owners would start looking for troublemakers to evict there first.

Tonight's meeting is a public one, and they're expecting plenty more people to show up from both complexes. As I wend my way through the parking lot, I try to recall the essentials of that first meeting—who they are, what or who put them where they are, what they want, and where they want to go. When I started

---

being plundered by the capacity of electronic devices to gather and manipulate data. But ordinary citizens don't have access to much of the data that've been gathered, and have at best only partial use of the gathering and manipulating technologies. Meanwhile, the material resources of the planet are declining faster than ever. So is our ability and will to halt the decline.

To say this so openly and blandly, however, is to pitch forward into the fact-free darkness of sentimental prophesy: Armageddon, the Apocalypse, the millennium, eco- or moral-slime decay and destruction. All of those are easy to *believe* in uncritically. The

working with them I thought I had all the answers. Now I'm not sure. Back then, I had a clear idea of what *I* wanted them to be and what I wanted them to achieve. But people always have their own identities and agendas.

That makes me look at my own agenda. What were my purposes in choosing them to organize? Who and what am I to them? Most of them like me well enough as someone to talk to, but talk is cheap. So far, the only one who trusts me is Candy, and I'm not sure why. For all I know I resemble her father, or a nonviolent version of her husband.

I've been careful not to spend any time alone with her. Sure, the usual ideas have occurred to me. Several times. But everything else in her world screws her, and she sure as hell doesn't need me adding to the list. Candy's the kind of woman who's never going to run short of men, and there's quite a few other items she needs more right now than another man crawling across her stomach on a temporary basis.

That's crude, but it's true. I'm here to help, not get laid. And even though I've gotten my head straight about Candy Basalle, I've had unexpected trouble sorting out what the real issues are: What do people here need? What's the exact nature of their deprivation?

As I said, I'm not sure. They *say* they need better recreation

---

ugly planetary realities millenarian rhetoric hides is blindingly seductive—as are, until you penetrate the low-density pixel matrix they appear in, the grinning assholes who front the various movements.

More disturbingly, all of it is equally easy to ignore, probably because it's just too fucking awful to think our way past what the millenarians are saying to what they really mean. The processes by which both uncritical belief and indifference are arrived at are more or less the same.

Yet the human community is losing something essential, and

facilities, and they keep coming back to that loaded word again and again: *recreation*. But when I ask them what they'd like to see done or built and how they propose to accomplish it, they look puzzled. They want *me* to define their needs and then, somehow, to satisfy them.

That one I've got the correct answer for: *No, I'm just an organizer.* What that means, I explain, is that I don't live here, that I don't feel your specific anxieties, and I don't have your experience of what's wrong.

So far, I've got one woman to trust me, and three others who are rationally convinced, more or less. But no one else. The rest still don't get it. They think only experts know what's true and what to do about it. Just as they still think the government is there to help them.

All right, I tell myself, this is the crux of the dilemma: the people who have the problem can't process it effectively. Since the translation medium of all experience is language, the obvious move to make is to examine the way they define need. These people invariably define most of their needs in terms of recreation.

Recreation is a loaded word, if ever there was one. Implicit in its use is a desire for a re-created environment and a re-created life. But these people want someone else to do it—me, the

---

nearly everyone senses it. It is something that won't sit still for quantification, still less for qualification. But losing it is making some of us very, very uneasy.

It isn't going to be like losing your car or your lover. What has been happening is much more complicated than that, and the effects are easily disguised. The loss isn't going to be apprehended by lunatic vision, and it sure as hell isn't going to be something you can catch in the newspapers or television news, or pick up prettily packaged at your local drugstore.

THE CRIME, AND THE VICTIMS

government. For them, recreation means distractions—they want an exercise facility, better shopping, more or clearer television channels, better antidepressant drugs. In the face of the multiple oppressions of daily life, the real goal they have is to be privately beautiful, and to be alone—with permanent and ready access to an anechoic chamber or a sensory-deprivation tank. The rest of the world be damned.

Recreation, it turns out, poses deeper difficulties than creation does. Around here you see how the Akron Design Center fulfills half-articulated desires by enfolding them into its heartless agenda. And how we're all damned by it becomes almost visible.

These are the material facts: Cottonwood Estates seems like an eloquent argument for public housing. It is a privately owned and operated seven-acre complex of some 260 apartments, blocked in twenty semidetached three-story wood-frame walk-up tenements. About one thousand people live in the complex, roughly 50 percent of them children. Sixty percent of the households are headed by female single parents, a large percentage of whom subsist on social assistance programs of a variety of types.

Apartment design in all the complexes is early Akron Design Center, circa 1955. Cottonwood Estates was built ten to fifteen years after the original Akron Design design was first perpe-

---

To discover—or uncover—what it is, I need a precise analytical method to guide me. Common sense won't help, and neither will divine inspiration or mystical insight. This is a truly post-Heraclitean dilemma—staring at a river, understanding that there is surface and depth to it, a general downstream motion and a morass of shifting, twisting currents, and recognizing that all homiletic reasonings are useless. If I step into this river I will get wet, I might drown, the currents might take me anywhere (or nowhere) downstream. Then I look up and see the water flowing

trated, time for the service bureaucracies and developers to make the few adjustments needed to render them perfectly profitable, and almost perfectly unlivable.

The apartments in the complex are paradigms of what developers and commercial architects call functionalism—which means that the builders make a big profit building them, the owners make a big profit running them, and the tenants can kiss ass and fend for themselves. The wide stretches of pavement provide perfect access for fire department vehicles and ambulances, and the internal structure and building entrances are designed to minimize fire damage—which pleases the insurance companies and almost no one else.

In short, these complexes are functional and efficient for everyone but the people who live in them. Tenants carry their garbage down long hallways filled with the tenement stink of cooked cabbage and broccoli to a common Dumpster that is equally convenient for collection companies and rats, and they park their cars in a common parking lot that is more convenient for vandals, car thieves, and repo artists than for them.

From the edges, Cottonwood looks innocuous enough. Most people would drive by without a thought as to how or why or by whom it was built. But as I walk along a path between two of the rows of buildings and into a concrete courtyard dotted with

---

over my head and wonder why I haven't drowned already. *Then* it comes to me, with the full impact of contemporary science and art: *I can't get out of this river. No one can.*

So, pragmatist that I am, I give in to the apparent chaos of present consequences and try to trace fundamental causes along a nearly infinite choice of routes. Nothing in my training tells me how to do this.

In the old kind of world, there were guides. Orpheus had Hermes, Abraham had his angels, Dante had his Virgil. Even Joe McCarthy had his Roy Cohn. It was possible, at least at times, to

people trying to carry on different kinds of recreation, my sense of reality quickly starts to decay. The complex is an apparently infinite labyrinth of artificial surfaces. The only visible exits are straight up, and the "landscape" consists of a series of asphalt and concrete terraces, each surrounded by buildings. Each terrace is loosely designed for some form of recreation, the most important of which appear to be parking and working on old, obsolete cars. On the rooftops I can see at least six satellite dishes, all pointed skyward to snag Detroit or Atlanta. From the angle I can't tell which.

If you're willing to accept parking as a form of physical and mental recreation, there's nothing *but* recreation facilities here. But what's also instantly visible is that except for parking lots, few of the facilities are being used for their designed purposes. In one courtyard two teenagers are throwing a Frisbee. A young couple is playing netless badminton in the middle of a parking lot, their baby carriage nestled carefully between two derelict cars. Some very young children are playing tackle tag, and about a dozen more people are simply milling around like zombies in a scene from *Dawn of the Dead.*

To my left, a group of kids are playing ball hockey in a pit that was originally a tennis court. About twenty people are standing along the galvanized fence watching them. On the other side is a

---

rely on instinct or will or (maybe) divine inspiration. But the only guide I have is a conviction that there's a kind of black spot near the center of everything. Something is deadly wrong inside all our heads, something that does not derive naturally from our intellectual heritage or from the conditions we are facing. I have that conviction, and the impulses that derive from it. The sum total of that conviction and its impulses is Public Eye, the persona who is transparently fronting this book.

He and I believe that it is likely that nothing and no one put the human species on this planet, or provided us with language and

terrace similar to the one I'm walking along. On the third side is one of the apartment buildings, and on the fourth an enclosed swimming pool. The total effect is visually confusing. The randomness of the human activity contradicts the geometric pattern of the buildings and terraces.

I'm looking for the day-care center, where the public meeting is being held. I've come a half hour early to have another look at the complex, and to see what people do here at this time of day. It's a warm summer night, the year's first, and I head for the swimming pool, not quite knowing why except that I assume children will be there.

Surprisingly, the swimming pool is deserted. I circle around the building to the entrance, and step inside. The air is thick with the smell of chlorine, the water is rippled, and I can hear pumps running. It's working okay, but no one is using it. I leave this puzzle unsolved and head down a stairway into the tennis court where the kids are playing hockey.

I stop there and break up a stick-swinging brawl between two kids. One of them, the aggressor, is crying—he explains through his tears that the other kid slashed him across the shins with his stick, and that he has to pay him back.

I calm him down, check his bloodied shin, and try to convince him it was an accident and that revenge isn't needed. The adults

---

consciousness. At best, organic life is the consequence of an arbitrary series of relatively inevitable, coactive coincidences. Earth is a small but highly organized agglomeration of particles in the right place at the right time. But in the logic trammels of the universe, human consciousness is a wild inference, one that breaks every known rule.

Notwithstanding, the human species is here and we have language and intelligence to prove it. For us, there are identifiable causalities. The moralist in me wants to say that it is the purpose of human life to understand those causalities as thoroughly as

THE CRIME, AND THE VICTIMS

standing along the fence watch me with an odd indifference. Not their kids.

"Are you a teacher?" the kid asks, calm enough now to wonder why I stopped the fight.

"No," I answer. "I just don't like seeing kids fighting with hockey sticks. Where's the day-care center?"

"At the far end. You have to go up there"—he points to the walkway I'd been on—"and along there until you see the concrete fence. Then go down, I think."

I thank him and walk back up the stairs. At the top I start to go in the wrong direction. The kids correct me by yelling, "No, stupid, it's *that* way," pointing in the right direction with their hockey sticks.

Feeling sheepish, I wave back and wander off in the right direction. As I pick my way through the multileveled maze of parking lots and unused recreation facilities, I'm struck by the emptiness of the place. It's a warm evening, but few people are outside, and only four or five tenants are out on their balconies. Only one couple is barbecuing. A thousand people live here. Where are they all? What are they doing?

I try to see the place as if I were one of the Cypress people, but it's too surreal to make the jump. I recall that the kids had no names for the various structures in the complex. They were

---

possible—a sacred duty of democratic citizenship. I won't say that. Not quite. It suffices to say that to fail in understanding them puts us at a terrible risk. Ignorance is an even greater danger in this hypertech civilization than it was to the first cave dwellers. And for us, now, it is not merely a hungry saber-toothed tiger that waits outside the cave to devour us.

Let me recapitulate: biological life, miraculous as it is, is probably the net outcome of an impenetrable nexus of cosmic and geophysical coincidences. But the *world*—the sum total of human impulses, actions, and interactive consequences—can and

reduced to pronouns and adverbs—"go along *there* until you run into *something,* then go *there,"* and so forth. Is this an intentional design feature, or is it design mediocrity and bad planning? I try to imagine a symbolic site plan, but that fails too. Rat maze, labyrinth, jungle. None of those, and all of them. The complex is stupid and it's ugly, but you can't quite make a case for deliberate malevolence.

I'm still thinking about this when I find myself in front of the day-care center. It's a converted ground-floor, two-bedroom apartment. Through the window I can see thirty-five or forty people inside, and that the meeting has started. I've lost half an hour without knowing how or where.

Shit. I'd wanted to be early, so I'd be able to keep the municipal planner, a guy named Murray Sterk, from sitting at the head table. Sterk means well, but he's the kind of person who grins while he's talking. I don't trust people who do that. It's too damned easy to picture them in Nazi uniforms grinning out phrases like "I'm sorry but I'm going to have to send you and your family to Belsen."

You understand the effect. And anyway, Sterk works for the municipality, and the municipality doesn't want to give these people anything more individual than welfare.

I walk across the shallow patio and slide open the glass patio

---

must be made sense of. Intelligence demands that we understand; language demands that we spread our understanding. It's either that or become scavengers of a planet we are willing to let die— small, competitive enclaves of activity operating on shallow focus. Okay for declining quadruped scavenger species like wolves or hyenas, but not for an aggressive species of five billion.

As the creator of Public Eye, I feel compelled to add up the human universe, and then to locate and describe the sources of the unease I feel about its chances of surviving.

That compulsion has a genesis that may be worth relating. It

THE CRIME, AND THE VICTIMS

door. The atmosphere inside is palpably close and irritable. Sterk is sitting behind a card table at the front of the room discussing the minutes of the last meeting. The minutes, of course, haven't arrived because Candy Basalle is the secretary and she gave them to me. I wave them at Sterk and suggest we hold up the start of the meeting for a few more minutes so those who are still coming in won't miss anything. I can see that people want a little informal talk—heads are turning, eyes are focusing on the faces that most interest them. Sterk doesn't answer, but the murmur in the room is positive. I win.

Sterk knows that my purposes are different from his. He eyes me with open suspicion, not quite sure how different they are. His aims are more different from those of the people here than mine are from his. These people want something to happen, and so do I. Sterk wants nothing to happen. For him, this is a damage-control situation.

The small advantage I have is that my method involves staying firmly in the background and opening up processes that will lead the actual protagonists to get what they need and want by themselves. His method is the opposite. He's looking at the meeting as a dramatic event in which he is the focus of attention—the bearer of news, gifts, and reassurances that everything is basically A-OK. Since things aren't A-OK here, he's in real trouble.

---

begins with growing up in a small town in northern British Columbia. As small towns go, mine was nothing special except that it was very new, growing very fast—and its urban infrastructure was constantly visible.

During the time when the deep structures within my brain were falling into place, sewers and water mains were being put into the environment around me, replacing the private wells and septic fields of the first pioneers. Electrical infrastructure likewise was being set in place or was being enlarged and reset to new standards. And because the construction of new housing was a con-

I can already feel him going over his list of intimidatingly political expressions: *big picture, infrastructure, fiscal responsibility.*

When you cut the camouflage from Sterk, he's a guy who cares most deeply about his own career, and that doesn't involve taking any responsibility for the lives other people are forced to live. If nothing good happens here tonight that will be just ducky from his professional point of view. He's going to try to control what occurs, and as an official of the municipal government he'll try to ensure it's nothing "political."

I check the room for other outsiders. There are a few and I'm surprised to discover I know them by name. Norm Haskins from the Welfare Department is at the back of the room. He's convinced that if these people get more services, they might develop some self-dignity, and get off welfare. Okay by me. Les Fortin, newly elected to the municipal council, is zeroing in on a group of women near the door. He's already looking to the next election, and there'll be votes here if he plays his cards right. Over in a corner is Bob Ball, the transactional analyst. He's talking to an attractive woman I haven't seen before—client hunting, no doubt, talking communications gibberish. He's a scumbag, but he's harmless. Then there's a surprise. Jock Olson is here.

Olson calls himself an educational consultant. I've been running into him in places like this for years. He fools around with

---

stant, the transformation of landscape it created became an unavoidable preoccupation. It was easy to see how and where individual and family life connected to civil life and its collective infrastructure. The subconscious conclusions I drew were probably unavoidable.

One of those conclusions was that my life and that of my family were tied to that of others, not by value or sentiment, but by physical apparatuses that were part of the necessary design of civil existence. Nothing I have subsequently learned or been propagandized by has denied or shaken my focus on that kind of

THE CRIME, AND THE VICTIMS

video cameras, making films for government agencies involved in what they call human development and what I call poverty maintenance. No one I've ever talked to has seen one of his films.

I have a halfhearted hunch that he's CIA. This time he's brought a friend with him, a beautiful woman in her late thirties. I've seen her around town, but never with him. She has an air about her of—what is it?—being more comfortable in her private imagination than in the world.

All my danger lights start flashing. Jesus H. Christ. If I'm thinking stupid thoughts like that I must be attracted to her. She's the most attractive female in the place, but that shouldn't mean I ought to be spinning out the way I am doing, creating a sentimental fantasy that has no relation to the organization or the difficulties these people are facing. Exotica. But you're interested in her too, right?

Okay, I'll tell you her story. Several years ago she was raped and beaten up in a university parking lot while acting as a decoy for a bunch of vigilantes who were trying to catch a rapist who'd raped and beaten a number of women in the same general vicinity. Something went wrong, and the rapist got her while the vigilantes sat twiddling their thumbs a hundred yards away.

I don't think the vigilantes ever did catch the rapist, and the woman spent a long time in the hospital. Reconstructive surgery,

---

perception. I was part of a powerful and numerous species forced by our growing numbers to live and act collectively. It was my first social truth and one that astonished and delighted me. But as I've grown older it has begun to fill me with fear.

Nearly everything—from physics through biology, genetics, and ecology, and on to the things that have occupied most of my adult life—urban planning, literature, and the pursuit of sexual pleasure—substantiates that original model of human life. We're connected, and the quality of life is directly dependent on the efficiency, accuracy, and unobtrusive interactivity of those con-

I think. I catch myself looking for the surgery scars on her face and neck and stop, guiltily. Our eyes meet for a second, but she doesn't know me from beans. I don't let on that I recognize her.

Why do I feel guilty? Well, certain varieties of consciousness cause blindness. My own native consciousness, which I should confess certainly isn't as a professional organizer, trains me to locate and develop idiosyncrasy and exotica. I should be concentrating on the other people in this room, the tenement dwellers of Cypress and Cottonwood Estates, to whom my organizational skills are of some use. They've got an organization birthing here. My job is to keep the various institutional leeches from attaching themselves to it and sapping its energies.

I'm useful to these people if I can help them to see their lives and their environment accurately enough that they are able to change it for themselves. If the other outsiders can delude them (or rather, continue to delude them), the result will be the kinds of services they have now—as appropriate to their needs as birdhouses for horses.

Another distraction appears, this one entirely welcome. Candy Basalle walks in—shiner and all. I'd like to cheer, but instead I guide her to the card table, drop the packet of minutes in front of her and make it clear to Sterk that he's sitting in her chair. He gets up with obvious reluctance, as Candy gives him a

---

nections, be they physical infrastructures like sewers and streets, social services like old-age pensions, health care, or unemployment insurance, or the less tangible systems that enable us to care for and touch one another—or merely let us talk across the fence with our neighbors.

It wasn't the connectedness of the human community that frightened me. With the typical directness of a child I was seeing that something else was going on across that late and modest frontier, a corollary phenomenon that continues unchecked in the globalized community I now find myself part of. Back then,

THE CRIME, AND THE VICTIMS

fish-eye stare that would peel paint from a wall. He finds a chair and sits down next to her. That's fine with me, since he'll be now uncomfortably sideways to the room, and Candy's body English will let everyone know he isn't to be trusted.

The meeting gets under way, but by the time it's half an hour old I'm convinced that this'll be the last meeting. The apartment managers have all been invited, which is like inviting the Gestapo to join the Resistance. Sterk's idea, no doubt.

The apartment manager from Cottonwood Estates is a large, severe-looking woman in her fifties. The manager from Cypress Estates is her mirror opposite, small, tanned, and surprisingly young. A third apartment manager from a smaller complex across the street doesn't identify herself, but makes a production out of writing down the name of everyone who speaks, interrupting speakers to get the spelling of their names correctly.

They're trying to intimidate the tenants, and they're doing a reasonably good job. Nobody here wants to confront those who have real and tangible power over them. Since most of the Cypress people go out of their way not to think of themselves as oppressed tenement-dwellers, they cling to the middle-class illusion that the managers—like anyone in authority—are their friends. If they don't kindle some hostility soon, it will leave the managers free to identify and possibly evict those who emerge as

---

what my community was doing to make life easier, more convenient, and shinier for ourselves was *always* visibly at the expense of the natural world. When a new subdivision was built, the forests we played in disappeared. When the sewer system was connected, the rivers filled with scum and filth.

This may sound as if it's leading up to a hippy-dippy complaint from the 1960s—we're losing our sacred connection with Mother Nature, and so maybe we ought to smoke some dope and tune in better, and so forth. . . . Actually, what I was on to is pretty much the opposite. From the very first, it was evident to me that

leaders. Candy, I suspect, will be the first to go. I've got to do something without being seen as manipulating.

Unwittingly, Sterk does it for me by changing the subject. He announces that he's gone to the mayor on their behalf, about the need for a local park. The mayor has responded predictably—pointing out the difficulties of land acquisition, and of resetting priorities in the middle of a budget year. He'll look into it, and will do what he can. Next year, mañana.

"Fucking asshole doesn't even know we're here," someone mumbles audibly from the back of the room.

Whoever said it is dead right, and a few people break out laughing. The apartment managers bob up and down in their chairs trying to spot the speaker. I have to suppress a grin. I can't afford to appear cynical, so I point out that getting a park won't solve all the problems. I suggest they draw up a list of the other things they need and hold the park question for discussion in that context. A tall, cadaverous young guy sticks up his hand and asks me if I can see about getting the speed limit cut to twenty mph.

"I've seen kids two years old out there on the street and why can't we get the police to enforce the speed limit we already have?" shouts a middle-aged woman with a hot pink bandanna around a headful of curlers.

---

human beings are different from nature, and that we have no choice about altering nature. Even then I didn't like many of the alterations we were making. They seemed too careless and head-long.

I still don't like most of our alterations, or our methods of making them. But going back to the squirrel hole or to the caves isn't an alternative. As a Northerner I knew that it was cold out there, and that we human beings weren't born with fur coats. We were born with unusually large brains, and brains are what we have to operate with, for better or worse.

THE CRIME, AND THE VICTIMS

Someone else yells, "That's because the bastards are out on the South Road giving us speeding tickets for making left turns into the complex."

Everyone laughs. I explain to them that I'm not going to do anything for them. Then I stick my neck out a little further and say that they should realize that the civil service generally isn't set up to help citizens. It's set up to keep things the way they already are.

"Look," I say, shuffling around a little for effect, "what civil servants do best is write memos to one another about how things should, but can't, be done. They're even better at filing those memos in large filing cabinets and forgetting about them."

This gets a laugh too. So does a police siren that has risen to a crescendo while I'm making my little speech. At least they have a sense of irony. Then someone comes in to say that a child has just been hit out on the road.

About half the people in the room rush outside to take a look. I follow, but it's not what everyone thinks. A police cruiser has chased a car into one of the parking lots, and two officers are rousting their suspect across the hood of his car. I watch as they cuff him and push him into the back of the cruiser. They're gone as suddenly as they came.

I bump into Candy in the parking lot. She tells me it's a guy

---

From the moment old Heraclitus sat down on the banks of that obscure Mediterranean river back in the sixth century B.C. and began to ponder the distinct "nature" of human consciousness, the human species has been involved in a fundamentally different game than the rest of the universe. Now the game seems to be changing again, or accelerating to a speed that makes the kind of play-by-play commentary Heraclitus invented impossible.

There are important differences between the infrastructure of contemporary civilization and that of the civilizations of the past. The obvious differences are in scale and complexity. The less

from her building. "He broke his parole or something," she says indifferently. "Happens all the time."

As the crowd starts to break up, someone spots another looming disaster. On the third-floor balcony of an adjoining building a small boy has climbed up on the railing and is half-hanging over the edge. Below the child is a ring of children, and a woman on the next balcony is leaning calmly on one elbow watching. In fact, everyone is watching, except for one woman, who is screaming at the top of her voice at the child to get down. A young guy in blue jeans dives into the building entrance and can be heard pounding up the stairs. Just as the child begins to slip, a young woman—presumably his mother—leaps through the balcony doors, catches the boy's wrist, and jerks him roughly off the railing. The young guy must have warned her.

Oohs and aahs. The mother wales the tar out of the child right out on the balcony, oblivious to the crowd watching.

"Why can't we force the goddamned developer to make those balconies safe?" a woman asks of no one in particular as we're filing back into the day-care center. "My Sarah fell off ours last summer," she continues, with the same distracted air of someone talking to God or to hidden microphones. "We live on the second floor, but she still fractured her skull. One of these days someone's kid is going to be killed."

---

obvious but more important differences are in structure and in system logic. They're all fundamental and crucial differences. Among other things, they explain why, in November 1925, Rainer Maria Rilke wrote to Witold von Hulewicz that the world was disappearing.

Anyone who thinks about it for longer than ten seconds will recognize that the physical and social infrastructure of contemporary industrial civilization has grown immensely in extent and complexity during this century. Sure. That was inevitable. We

The apartment manager winces and bites her lip, but before she can answer, a dried-up-looking middle-aged woman—one of the tenants—answers for her. "It's not the developer that's at fault, it's the parents. They just don't care."

I catch myself questioning who is right. No one can make the world perfectly safe. And anyway, safety's not the problem and it sure as hell isn't the solution. People need to have a method of caring—one that renews itself and is rewarded—and they have to know how to care effectively in the first place. If the mother whose child was out on the balcony rail is incompetent at caring, whose fault is it?

Sure, it's her fault. Then you have to ask how she got here in the first place, where nobody in her right mind would live if she had the choice. If she hadn't chosen this particular complex, her only alternative would have been a mind-numbing series of identical places.

Or is that just me exerting my middle-class tastes? Maybe there's nothing wrong with Cypress Estates. Nothing life-threatening, or inherently unhealthy. There are places to park cars, watch television, take baths. A shopping mall is within walking distance, and there are schools for the children. No terrorists, and only occasional rapists and muggers. No one has dropped a nuclear weapon on the complex, so far. Are people

---

need it to deal with our increased populations, and to facilitate the exercise of our technological and consumer wealth.

Social infrastructure should simplify existence, and for a while, roughly a single decade just after WWII—it did. For some classes of society, it continues to. But what it is now doing for and to the vast majority of citizens in the postindustrial democracies—the West—is more or less the opposite.

Explaining why and demonstrating how requires penetrating the structural heart of the economic system to analyze the rela-

supposed to overthrow the government because there is a short-age of green space, or because vandalism is an uncurbed problem, or because the television satellite dish is out of order, leaving a choice of only the six or seven local cable channels? Am I merely exercising taste here?

In one sense, yes. Given my particular tastes, none of these people would live here. Okay, asshole. So where would they live? They would live where I do. And where would I then live?

The meeting starts again. People are now talking openly about things that bother them, but they're careful, as always, not to speak of them as personal problems.

"There should be a place for battered women," says one woman. "Someplace safe," she adds, looking at Candy.

Before that can go anywhere interesting, another woman says she wants "those damned long-haired teenagers to wear proper bathing attire, because they leave their filth in the pool." When someone cuts in to point out that she's never used the pool anyway, the woman snaps back that she doesn't swim in it because it's too filthy. "Get management to regulate things bet-ter," she proclaims.

The managers get themselves into trouble all on their own over this one. One of them explains that it's difficult, that it takes time. I can't help myself—I roll my eyes. Candy catches me

---

tionship between corporate dynamics and government regula-tory patterns, and examining the shifts that have occurred be-tween capital, labor, and investment. I don't know enough to do that. Do you?

Let's see if a metaphor will open it up a little. How about we extend the game metaphor a little? For instance, it's obvious that you can't play the big game of life inside a cardboard box, and you can't play your game very well if the grass on the field hasn't been cut, right?

Well, you can if the game has been turned into a video game,

doing it and laughs out loud. There's a ripple of hoots and groans from the audience.

Several people want higher speed bumps inside the complex, without the drainage openings that enable motorcyclists to scoot through without slowing down. Management will look into it. But anything done will come back on the tenants. Higher costs mean higher rents, or higher taxes for the taxpayers. Management will look into the costs and let the people know.

"When will that be?" It's the same unidentified voice I'd heard earlier. I can't pick out the speaker. It's a female voice, but it seems to come from everywhere and nowhere.

"It takes time. It took two months to get the bumps installed in the first place."

"When?" The voice insists. *"When?"*

"We'll let you know."

"When?" a new voice echoes.

"When we get the facts together."

From the back of the room the phantom whispers, *"Bullshit."* Everyone in the room hears her.

Just before the meeting breaks for coffee, Sterk and I tangle one last time. He announces that after the break he'd like to see a chairman elected for the next meeting.

"Any chairperson for these meetings should come from inside

---

but then it isn't quite real. The game of life is big and organic and the stakes are as high as they can get. You can't put a can of Coke on top of it, but you can, perhaps, play—and possibly better—with no grass at all if the field has been Astroturfed. But first you've got to install and then pay for the Astroturf. But once you've done that you've got to install lights for night play because you'll need to draw large crowds to pay for the Astroturf. Meanwhile you'll have found that you need referees and statisticians, and that you'd better buy first-rate protective equipment to prevent injuries and keep your insurance policies intact. You also

the complex," I say, emphasizing the gender neutralization. "And why not elect a slate of officers for the organization?"

The evening is cooling rapidly, but it's hot and sticky inside the day-care center. I slip outside and walk along the side of the building. It isn't just a matter of my taste, I decide. The complex is falling apart. Doors are scraped, concrete cracked, plaster falling. I try to imagine the place twenty years from now, but that's impossible. The social imagination that created Cottonwood Estates has substituted the future with a concept of real estate profits. This place can't grow old because nothing but the people who live in it are designed to grow old. The complex won't age. It'll only break down and cease to function.

I recognize that there's an odd sort of bacchanalia going on here just the same. No grapes are involved, no ivy, no wine or vintage, and very little physical ecstasy. It's simple extension, creation, development, profit, a bizarre ménage à trois of economic gain and rubble and plastic. Even the stars look fake here, and the night air stinks of stale piss and Styrofoam.

Coffee and donuts are being served when I go back inside. Someone passes me a tray of shriveled brownies. I try one, and it tastes as bad as it looks.

---

have to pay for association with the appropriate league or society, and you may even need to buy a franchise. All of that costs money, so much that pretty soon you have to form a corporation and sell shares on the stock market. And at that point you're so enmeshed in an alternate logic that the game doesn't belong to you anymore.

I'm not sure if most people recognize the extent to which such things have redefined subsistence and citizenship. There is an intangible point in any society at which poverty begins, and citizenship effectively ceases. For a primitive tribesman on the North

But despite my pessimistic predictions, the rest of the meeting is Sterk's nightmare, not mine. Forty-two people kick in two dollars each and sign up as members. Predictably, the prestige offices go to males: a delivery-truck driver named Ross Hughes is elected chairman, someone I've never seen before named Al Robles is vice-chairman. Candy Basalle is secretary and Tina Sordo, another of the women I've been chatting up, is treasurer. They appoint a delegation to approach the school board for free recreation time at a nearby school, and another delegation to appear before the City Council for speed-limit changes. Candy is going to write to the post office about getting a mailbox in the complex. Norm Haskins and Les Fortin offer to help them. Jock Olson takes out his video camera and films the election for posterity and for all I know, the CIA. In case it's the latter I make sure I'm not in his movie by getting up and standing next to him while he films.

Ross Hughes gets caught up in an ecstasy of democracy. He seems to think that he can solve any problem by having a vote on it. The women are wiser. It's clear to me they're eventually going to run the organization because they're the ones who live here all the time. There are eight different votes, all unanimous. The last one is an agreement to meet again in one month's time. Candy Basalle catches my eye and winks, grimacing because she used the bruised eye. I wink back, painlessly.

American plains two hundred years ago, subsistence might have required a horse, some homemade weapons and utensils, animal skins, along with enough food and the social companionship and military support of other members of the tribe. On our terms such a life might not have been easy or sweet, but the tribesman would have considered him- (or her-) self wealthy, and certainly on relative terms would have had full political and economic rights. Able to remain socially and privately visible, in other words.

Compare that situation to the material array required for visibility today, and you'll see what I'm getting at. Compare it to what

They're the Cypress Neighborhood Improvement Association and some of them look pleased, a few look a little frightened. But one or two are gazing around the room with a brand-new sense of their own importance, and that of their group. They haven't re-created the world yet, but they're better off than they were.

---

was needed even as recently as the turn of the century, and it will become even clearer. An average of about ninety days of labor annually provided subsistence in Uruk five thousand years ago. And until the Industrial Revolution, few societies required very much more of their citizens to generate subsistence and/or basic visibility. At the turn of the century the operant currency was still human labor, and full citizens able to work hard and exercise a moderate degree of intelligence—at least in North America—could have a good life. Now life is commodity accumulation, manipulation, and information. Totally different.

THE CRIME, AND THE VICTIMS

AKRON DESIGN CENTER ANTIDOTES
Professionals

Time for a major counterattack on professional egos and privileges.

a: All medical doctors must display signs on their office, home, and automobile doors revealing gross and net annual incomes, along with a statement of nonmedical assets and the location and duration of all vacations in the past three years.

b: Lawyers will be given the option of dressing in clown or vampire costumes during court trials, and are prohibited from entering restaurants and bars after ten P.M. unless wearing their chosen court costumes. They are also prohibited from wearing business or leisure suits at any time.

c: All certified accountants must wear open necked shirts, gold neck chains, and pastel-colored leisure suits during business hours. They will be obligated to stand whenever a client sits down.

d: Every architect involved in designing residential developments larger than fifty units must live in the development and work as a caretaker for a period of one year. This would ensure more socially responsive design and would relieve unemployment within the pro fession.

e: Offices for urban planners and architects must be relocated to the most economically depressed areas of cities, with street-level access

---

THE DIFFERENCE BETWEEN HUMAN AND OTHER SYSTEMS

All living organisms are systems. Most are relatively simple ones, others utterly complex. Taking this convenient metaphor a step further, one could say that complex organic life consists of hierarchies of systems, some acting cooperatively and symbiotically, while others are predatory and competitive. Others again are

109

for citizens. In addition, urban planners and architects must undertake the following every three years:

    i.) a self-paid two-month vacation to study the history and civic and aesthetic values of urban development.

    ii.) a six-month paid tour of duty in the PUS.

f: Public transportation planners and executives shall not be allowed to own or operate private motor vehicles, nor be allowed to travel in them during working hours.

g: Administrative professionals in all fields must wear brightly colored leotard-based costumes at all times during working hours.

h: All real estate transactions must be carried out in Latin or pig Latin.

i: All national and international sports federations will be disbanded and competitive "amateur" tournaments and spectacles beyond the civic level will be prohibited. The Olympic Games, in particular, will be discontinued on the grounds that they have become a hazard to public mental health and to the health of individual competitors. Paid professional athletes shall be required to pass literacy tests, with failure penalties going to fund the public library system and finance an educational pension system for the players. Salary caps will limit remuneration to 200 percent of the national average per capita income. Sixty percent of gross profits deriving from professional team sports shall go to support amateur sports.

j: Physical fitness will be tolerated and even encouraged, but within the context of mental fitness rather than as a professional life-style in itself. A 50 percent surcharge tax on earnings deriving from

---

parasitic. Neo-Darwinists and other believers in steady-state evolution would go further than that, proposing that the tensions within these hierarchies have led to human progress and its attributes: interpersonal and social competitiveness, economic and cultural class distinctions, and social violence.

Without arguing the validity of the metaphor, let's look at the strict nature of complex systems—organic, mechanical, or cybernetic—and determine the unifying features. All systems appear to have an internal dynamic, *a prime directive*, as it were.

THE DIFFERENCE BETWEEN HUMAN AND OTHER SYSTEMS

aerobic-fitness institutions would accrue to the public library system. Signs shall be prominently placed in fitness facilities warning participants of the dangers of brain damage from bouncing. The current rule requiring exercisers to grin at all times will be rescinded as a safety hazard.

Whatever the explicit purpose or nature of the system, the most powerful element of that internal dynamic is identical to the fundamental goal of organic life: to continue to function, to survive, and to extend and impose its operating logic and system parameters on adjacent systems, whether they are inherently competitive or not.

In human beings, consciousness of self isn't an integral part of that prime directive, even though it frequently functions as its tool. In fact, it is the one element that tends to subvert the prime

111

SOUL WALKER

I was sitting in one of the bars at La Guardia Airport, waiting for a flight and trying to dig my way out of the vague depression I experience whenever I travel. Two men in business suits talking at the next table weren't helping.

"Did you get those futures under control before you left the office?" the older of them asked the other. I'm not normally an eavesdropper, but his peculiar use of the word "future" instantly captured my attention.

Both men were dressed in Akron Design Center standard combat issue: suits gray to blue, eyes gray to blue, underwear no doubt the same. Both were carrying briefcases with copies of *In Search of Excellence* placed to display conspicuously when opened. I noted the older one's suit was slightly darker, and that his voice exuded seniority if not quite authority. Or maybe it's just that I didn't like the idea of him controlling futures *and* wielding authority.

---

directive, because self-consciousness implies a capacity to discriminate between self and external occurrences, events, and (particularly) consciousnesses: "otherness."

Human awareness of *otherness* has generated its own set of phenomena—respect, the kind of love Christians call *agape,* and a willingness to sacrifice personal autonomy and volition in order to protect the autonomy and volition of others. For a systems analyst, most of whom are neo-Darwinian determinists, this is the strangest of all the phenomena in the known universe, and the system they generate is unlike any other in nature.

THE DIFFERENCE BETWEEN HUMAN AND OTHER SYSTEMS

The other man seemed slightly uncomfortable with his question. "I tied down wheat and hog bellies, Hal," he answered, using the man's name as if it were a prayer rug he'd only recently gained the use of. "I've got the energies in my briefcase. They're all unstable as hell, Hal, and I thought we could work them over during the flight and wire our moves from Denver. I brought the laptop with me, so we can plug in by modem from the teleport terminal."

Hal grimaced. "Can't you handle this by yourself?" There was a slight edge of irritation in his voice.

"Hal, I need your help on this one," the younger man whined. "I just don't have enough experience in this kind of volatile market."

Hal gazed at the younger man, coiling his body in the chair as if he were about to impart a great truth—or to rip into his inferior's jugular. "Experience no longer exists, my friend," he said. "There's only data now, and the daring to recognize when it becomes profitable information."

Hal closed his briefcase as he said it, flipped a dollar bill into the center of the table, and placed his empty whiskey glass over it. The conference was finished and *In Search of Excellence* had triumphed over civilization once more. Both men slid out from behind the table, tugged the lapels of their suits straight, and

---

It is strange for two reasons. One is that this uniquely human operating system seems to have little or no instinct for self-preservation. Instead of protecting itself against change and foreignness, it invites both to its hearth. Its other strange property is what most people casually call civilization, the now-you-see-it-now-you-don't phenomenon Sam Johnson accurately insisted on calling *civility*—humane collective life. It is the only brake on the permanent violence of nature that has ever appeared—other than individual death and social or species extinction, of course, which are not systems at all, but rather the result of violent

walked to the entrance. The younger man walked just behind Hal's shoulder. He still didn't have a name.

The nameless asshole is openly displaying military deference, I thought, as I watched them disappear into the terminal crowd. Disgusting. I was glad they were leaving my universe. Then I realized that it was *their* universe *I* was in. At least I could be grateful that they were leaving the small part of it I was temporarily occupying, and I didn't want to know where they were going. Straight to hell, for all I cared. But with a stopover in Denver to manipulate the future.

To tell the truth, I didn't want to know where any of the grinning assholes still sitting in the lounge were going, where they'd been or why, or what they were calling themselves. I didn't want to be there. I wanted to be at home where I could think straight.

Travel scrambles my brain circuitry, air travel more than any other kind. There's probably no other kind of place on earth I dislike more than airports. They make me grumpier than I normally am, and I'm a reasonably grumpy person. I'd been traveling for weeks and right then I'd have given quite a lot to be nonconscious, and more if I could be at home. I certainly didn't want to talk to anyone.

I wasn't to get my wish. An elderly man entered the bar and

---

misadventure or degenerative biological collapse. Civilization is also the main challenge to neo-Darwinian determinism, conventional systems theory, and the radical conservatism in our economic and political spheres that is currently fueling all kinds of stupid and barbaric behavior.

In the evolution of organic life on this planet, complexity rather than simplicity has thus far been rewarded. Organisms have become increasingly complex, and in general have tended to express organizational complexity as specialization. But strict

THE DIFFERENCE BETWEEN HUMAN AND OTHER SYSTEMS

stood near the entrance, scanning the scattered clientele. Almost without hesitation, he focused on me. Our eyes met briefly. I broke contact first, developing a sudden urge to determine the species of wood used in the bar decor. I regretted that choice instantly. The table in front of me was walnut-grain Formica, a one-eighth-inch veneer over sawdust board. The wall panels were also ersatz walnut, the kind they photograph onto chipboard.

Unpleasant-looking old futzer, I decided as I gave in and watched the elderly man make his unerring way to my table. Something had gone dry in that face long ago, giving it a severity that masked his exact age. He might have been anywhere from his late fifties to early seventies. He moved easily enough, but there was nothing in his body language and demeanor that indicated the kind of weathering that creates the oaky wisdom that sometimes comes with age. He looked as if he were petrified.

The briefcase he carried intensified my instinctive dislike. It was an expensive leather one, neutral color, narrow and soft-sheened. No laptop in that one. This guy was from senior management.

Despite myself I wondered what was inside it. Plans for an industrial takeover? Plans for the end of the world? A leather-bound copy of *In Search of Excellence*?

---

specialization has the limitation of creating fragilities to environmental change. In the very recent past organic complexity has bifurcated into a new direction, rewarding a phenomenon we usually call intelligence, the peculiar ingredient that has begotten both civilization and its host of "natural" enemies—like neo-Darwinism and radical conservatism.

The special kind of intelligence human beings have developed is not quite the same as self-consciousness, although self-consciousness is one of its obvious preconditions. The human

There was a more immediate question: Why was he coming to pick on me? As he closed in, the expression on his face betrayed a strange sort of neediness. Well, then, he couldn't be an executive. The briefcase would therefore be filled with pamphlets. Pyramid sales, or some course on executive-building. Or worse—religious pamphlets. He had the look of a man bent on saving someone.

As he approached, I almost wished the Akron Design Center slimeoids hadn't left. I could have pointed to them—see, look! Those guys need your literature, not me.

I would have had my objections brushed aside. He was fixed on me like the Ancient Mariner on the Wedding Guest. Oh, Christ, I thought as he closed in.

"Christ can't help you," he said in a crisp accent with German undertones. "But perhaps I might."

I'd have rolled my eyes if there'd been anyone around to do it for. There wasn't, and anyway, it was too late. My elderly assailant was staring at me as if he could see through me. Maybe he could. He'd already read my mind.

"Airports are horrible places," he said.

"That's what I've been thinking," I said before I could stop myself.

"I'm aware of that," he said, his mouth sucking on his cosmic

---

species has come to dominate the planet because intelligence, freed from the threat of violence, has enabled creative adaptation, generalization, and curiosity. Human beings have succeeded as a species because they are curious generalists, and have therefore been able to move beyond simple subsistence to build physical, social, and psychological infrastructures that obviate conflict and violence and enable us to adapt quickly to a wide variety of conditions.

In case I'm sounding overly sanguine, let me point out that

THE DIFFERENCE BETWEEN HUMAN AND OTHER SYSTEMS

lemon again. "You're impressionable. That's why I chose you."

"Go away," I said feebly. "I don't want to be chosen."

"Well," he replied, fixing me with his cold stare, "you've been chosen. Stop sniveling and listen."

Maybe, I calculated, a show of aggression will get him to leave me alone.

He cut that thought off. "Don't try aggression," he said. "It won't get you anywhere. I'm here to help you, and there's no avoiding it."

"I don't need help. I'm just fine. Let me wait for my stupid plane in ignorance."

"Stupid ignorance."

"Pardon me?"

"You heard me," he said. "Planes aren't stupid. They aren't anything at all, one way or the other. They're machines. But you're stupid if you desire ignorance."

Well, I thought, at least he's not a born-again Christian. They love ignorance. It's their operational precondition. "I desire you to leave me alone," I mumbled. "That's what I desire."

"You're already far too alone. That's why I'm here."

This time I did roll my eyes. To hell with him. "Go away," I said. "Cease and desist. Let me bear the agony of travel unmolested by your wisdom."

---

on planetary terms, intelligence is a relative newcomer, and that it is lodged on an altogether narrow and shaky edifice. Intelligent life may turn out to be a short-term evolutionary dead end. It has already had a cataclysmic effect on the rest of the biosphere.

Thus far it has put both the planet and almost all its species onto a fog-shrouded promontory of technological initiative where what happens next is not at all secure or certain. On one side are planetary depletion and ecological collapse, and on the other, the

"Exactly," he said.

"What?"

"Travel is agony."

"You came here to tell me that?" I asked, interested despite myself.

He lowered himself gingerly into the chair opposite me. With our eyes at the same level I felt slightly less uncomfortable, but I still wanted him to go away. "No," he said solemnly. "I came to tell you why."

"You came to tell me why travel is agony?" I said. "I know why. It's because weird people are always hitting on me. Weird people like you."

The old man was unperturbed. "That isn't why, you ass, and you know it."

I didn't know, and I told him so. Then I repeated my request that he leave me to my discomforts.

"It's actually rather simple," he said. "It has to do with the travel abilities of the human soul."

Shit, I thought. "You're a Rosicrucian, aren't you?"

"No. Please listen carefully. The reason why you feel disoriented when you travel is because your soul isn't traveling with you."

"I don't have a soul," I said. That didn't sound right, so I

---

destruction of all life in nuclear pyrotechnics. But we're on that edifice, and we are (as a species) bound to enlarge it or to perish from our failure to do so. There is no turning back.

We can't any longer allow the human universe we've built around us to operate with models drawn from nature. Nature's systems are too crude. There're too many of us, and we can't risk the violence and conflict inherent in natural systems.

We may be even more alone than we've ever imagined. It isn't just that our operating system is different. It is, but we haven't been one with nature for at least three thousand years, not since

THE DIFFERENCE BETWEEN HUMAN AND OTHER SYSTEMS

corrected myself—better to discuss theology than personality. "There's no evidence for the existence of the soul."

At first he seemed to go for it. "There's no material evidence for the existence of the soul, you mean. Not conventional evidence, anyway. Don't underestimate me. *I'm* not a stupid man. We're both familiar with the philosophical arguments about the existence of the soul. They all proceed deductively from the phenomenon of human consciousness and memory. My argument is of a quite different sort."

"Go on," I said, curiosity overwhelming my misgivings.

"Let me give you an example you'll be familiar with. Some of the native cultures on the Northwest Coast have a saying. It's this: 'When a man (or a woman) abandons his home ground, he loses his soul.' Now, admittedly, that sounds like a syndicalist slogan until you examine a few illustrations."

"I'm listening." I *was* listening, against my will.

"If a multinational corporation were to purchase a plot of land next to the one you're living on, and announced that it intended to excavate a huge pit on it, what would you do?"

"Depends on what my piece of property was worth to me. And on how much the developer was willing to give me to get out."

"Multinationals don't give anything away. And how is value

---

self-consciousness massively enlarged the amount of system feedback, and changed its essential tonalities and intentions. The human system is an infinity of swirling contextualizations, a system logician's nightmare.

Out of a misplaced scientific enthusiasm for paradigmatic models of analysis and production, we may have placed ourselves in the hands of systems that are essentially hostile to our unique kind of intelligence.

Using nature as a model has led to the current economic and environmental crises we face. Natural models operate by over-

assigned to what you're calling property?" He paused for a second, as if to let the alternate taxonomies he was proposing penetrate. "Let me rephrase my question slightly. Imagine that there are two people living next to the target land. One was born on the spot, and his ancestors have lived there for at least several generations. The other has lived there for less than two years. Which one would be more likely to fight the multinational, and which one would be more effective?"

Those weren't very hard questions. "The homer, naturally. In both cases. He'd have reasons to stay and fight, and he'd be more likely to persist when the going got tough."

"Well," he said, "that's what the human soul is, and where it resides. It's a relationship between consciousness and material objects. It is a sensibility created by familiarity and loyalty to places and things. This might sound like a new kind of materialism, but it's really very old."

"Interesting," I said. "But what's this got to do with flying, or with hanging around airports?"

"Quite a lot. Think of airports as generators of homelessness. Or as repositories of physical and intellectual landscape alienation, petrie dishes of delocalizing despair. Think of them as soul debris depots. The first signal is that airports are much the same across the world. They're a home for the professionally homeless.

---

production, and by exploiting every lapse in aggression and capacity, always tilting the "market" balance in favor of those most capable of violence. Nature has always been capitalism's model, and in the current neo-Darwinian jihad, the two systems resemble each other more than ever before. The deductive "scientific" model on which Marxism is based is equally crude and equally violent, sacrificing flesh, bone, and common kindness to a theoretical model of historical inevitability. And as far as I can see, none of the currently shaky models deriving from contemporary

THE DIFFERENCE BETWEEN HUMAN AND OTHER SYSTEMS

But they're more than that, because of the alienated energies constantly passing through them and the residual buildup of that energy. They've become capable of creating alienation—actively disturbing and even destroying souls."

"This is getting awfully farfetched," I muttered.

"It's merely unconventional. I could explain the physics to you, but you're not a physicist. I'm explaining it in urban design terms and in anthropological terms, which are within your range of nominal expertise."

Right again, I thought, wondering if he was from the CIA. Too old, I decided. And too accurate. Far too weirdly accurate.

He went on. "The technology for creating antilocalist experiential structures has existed now for some years. The motivation researchers inside the major consumer corporations have been using it for decades without really recognizing what they've got. They understand, for instance, that there is a fundamental human need for familiarity and solidarity, and they've learned to manipulate its focus from landscapes and kinship or social loyalty structures to consumer stereotypes. They're like terrorists with a neutron bomb they can't explode, but recognize that the more they tinker with it the more radiation will be released."

"Can you give me a concrete example?"

---

physics and mathematics are going to help us, because none of them are improvements on nature, either.

This being the case, we'd better ask ourselves some fundamental questions. First, what does the human species have out here to work with?

Well, we have our curiosity, our ability to generalize and to contextualize. But to survive—to make the crucial adaptations that will allow life to continue on this planet past the next century—we now need something else. We need to contextual-

"Well, the Disney facilities are the most extreme ones."

"I've never been to one," I said. "Never will, either."

"Millions have, and millions more are going to go. Disney launders history, reshaping and cartoonizing its events and characters, and it does it to the world we're in. It encourages people to experience history and geography without any physical risk or threat to their values. But what it's really doing is translating the diversity of life into values designed to be easily digestible. Fish become fish sticks. Chickens become chicken nuggets. And then you go off to your local malls, which offer product simplifications that retool your everyday needs while you're shopping for them. Haven't you ever wondered why you feel odd after an hour or two at a mall?"

"I've thought about it quite often," I admitted. "I decided it was a result of being in an environment composed entirely of things other people *want* me to want without ever addressing what I might *need*. But what does this have to do with airports, or my soul? You're losing me."

"Well, think about Disney, the malls, consumerism in general, as an alternative to the human soul. Because there's no physical frame of reference or consequence in any of them, a soul can't find sustenance. It simply withers away."

"Uh-huh. That I can see. But maybe that's the way things

---

ize in a new way, and we need to learn to alter and control the material and energy consumption of the support systems we have created to handle our massive numbers. If we don't, they are going to destroy us.

The second, and more painful, question is this: What are we going to do about being out on this precarious promontory, with its crumbling cliffs on each side, and its acid-laced mists rolling ever more blindingly over us?

There are some choices. We can continue with the futurist comic book fantasies of the last fifty years and pretend we're not

are going. Maybe it's a natural evolution of the species."

"Oh, an evolution, perhaps. But not a natural one. It's closer to a devolution, or a convolution. And you'll have a hard time arguing that it's in the interest of the species. It will reduce our frame of reference in every conceivable way, wipe out our companion species, and eventually supplant nature itself with artificial technological environments. It will constrict the genetic pool and deactivate four-fifths of our earned intelligence. That's hardly a positive evolution."

"Those don't seem to be risks we can confront directly. They're happening. No way to stop them."

"I believe such a judgment is premature. I'm suggesting only that the alterations and the risks should be understood. Or rather, that *you* understand them."

The waiter was standing beside the table. "Is this man bothering you, sir?" he asked, motioning at the old man.

"No," I said. "Bring me another beer, will you?"

"What brand would you like, sir?"

The old man cut in. "Bring us two glasses of soda water. That will be just fine."

The waiter glanced sharply at me for confirmation. "Okay," I said. "He's my uncle. I'll drink soda water if he says it's good for me."

---

where we are, that we're really cosmic nomads on our way to conquer the stars. That one has become so threadbare it isn't going to work for very much longer, particularly since the space program is now thoroughly focused on military projects like satellite surveillance laser technologies aimed at zapping terrestrial enemies from near space.

Alternatively, we can pretend that life is a professional exercise and evaluate our options, in which case most of us will get depressed and go back to the first choice—slick up, buy a BMW, and go off hunting opportunities with the same ignorance of

"Don't be impertinent," the old man snapped. "Now. Let's get back to our discussion."

"Do you think we might get a little more specific?"

"Fine," he said. "The human soul has a very specific property that makes it hostile to airports and air travel."

"And what's that property?"

"It doesn't fly."

He stared at me coolly, as if expecting a negative response. Laughter, probably. I wasn't laughing. Instead, I was sorting through the logic of his previous statements. It was consistent.

"Are you speaking metaphorically, or are you making a declarative statement to the effect that a human soul is prohibited from boarding an aircraft."

"I see no difference."

"Well, I'd be interested to know why it can't board aircraft. There's nothing in the IATA regulations about it. I've read them. And surely it isn't the lack of seats."

"The soul is not a voluntary adjunct to your body," he answered, ignoring my witticism. "And it isn't an automatic possession. It can be earned and nurtured, just as it can be lost through inattention or destroyed by misadventure. And it is not automatically inherited. Several hundred million people, mostly in the industrial states, no longer have souls."

---

planetary context and environment our more innocent cavemen ancestors displayed while they hunted the antelope and buffalo.

Those responses are epidemic on a global scale right now, particularly in the technologized democracies. Governments in the 1980s have virtually ceased all serious long-range calculations, deferring the issue of planning to short-term economic development plans that are little more than propagandized strategies to aid short-term corporate profit-taking binges—one last roll in the gravy before the millennium.

THE DIFFERENCE BETWEEN HUMAN AND OTHER SYSTEMS

The confusion I was experiencing must have become visible, because he shifted his operating gloss from metaphysics to digital technology.

"Try to think of your soul as a data base that by its nature can't be teleported, and is only transportable at speeds that allow it to be physically experienced while in transit—at walking speed, in other words. It's only accessible *within* its specialized dataframe."

"Oh," I said, shifting in my chair as the waiter slid the two soda waters onto the table and smiled at me expectantly. I dropped him a five and he disappeared without making change. "That makes sense, I suppose. So where is my soul right now?"

The old man frowned, and began to stare at the back of his hand as if it were a television screen. After a moment's consideration, he looked up again. "You've been traveling for thirteen days?"

I nodded. "About that."

"Then your soul is somewhere between Berwick, Pennsylvania, and Stroudsburg, depending on whether it followed Interstate Eighty or walked from Cleveland as the crow flies."

He said it with such authority that I couldn't laugh. "It's following me?"

"Of course. It followed you from Akron to Cleveland, and when you flew east it followed you. What else would it do?"

If this doesn't scare you, it bloody well should. The system-collapse trajectories are deliberately *not being plotted*. But they exist, we're on them, and anyone younger than about fifty years old is almost certain to experience the business end of them. We're nonplanning a world that won't be habitable for our children and grandchildren.

This is one of the many points at which I tend toward paranoia. I have a lifelong, recurring fear that those in authority have given up, that they are accepting that the human species and the planet

"You said that the soul is landscape-derived. Why wouldn't it stay on home ground and wait for me to return?"

"You're indulging in personification. You're ascribing self-consciousness to something which exists as an element of human consciousness. The soul is the relationship between a neurally housed body of understanding and a physical environment. Once created, it can't survive without its body of understanding, so to speak. So it follows it, tries to locate it."

"All the way from Akron? That's about three hundred and seventy-five miles."

"Your soul is quite a fast walker," he said without a trace of irony. "It would walk all the way here, unless you underwent a personality change, or a loss of memory, or you died."

"Then it would die?"

"Not exactly. It would try to return to the locations and conditions of its creation."

"And do what?"

For the first time, the old man seemed slightly embarrassed. "It would, er, haunt. For a while. Nothing nasty, mind you. You may have noticed that places where people have lived a long time have a certain eerie coldness after they've gone."

I have, but I didn't say so. After my mother and grandmother moved from the boardinghouse—it was redeveloped—the old

---

are doomed. I experienced these sensations as a small child when I saw my first sewage outlet, and when I walked into my first clear-cut forest. The experiences seeded a combination of terror and rage that I've spent my life trying to harness.

As an adult, I see things slightly differently. Those in authority have simply been overwhelmed by the difficulties of imagining a future, and have therefore settled on perceptual methods that ignore it. Same scenario, same conclusions, except that I now tend to ascribe blame to bankrupt conceptual structures instead

THE DIFFERENCE BETWEEN HUMAN AND OTHER SYSTEMS

neighborhood had that quality. It was very spooky, actually.

"That's right," he said. "Almost a sense of betrayal. But those old places have always welcomed you back."

He was right. I've managed to visit the old places fairly regularly since I left, and it has always felt good, despite the destruction and the changes.

"That's because while you're there you've taken care to visit each important location," he interrupted. "Paying your respects to the memories, as it were. You may not recognize this, but your behavior there is highly ritualized. The places sense the kinship of your present soul, and nourish the connection."

I was getting used to having him read my mind. "I usually fly to get there. That means my soul isn't with me when I arrive."

"Smell," he answered. "The locations smell you, because you're from there."

"So what happens when I leave here and go home? Does my soul see me flying over it and start walking back?"

"Well, it senses your passage rather than sees you. That's why you feel disoriented for several weeks after a long trip. Your soul isn't there. And that's why there's a strong sense of mental disturbance for a few hours when it actually arrives back."

"Sort of like reentry impact? It must be pissed off when it arrives. All that walking for nothing."

---

of human beings with bank vaults where their brains are supposed to be.

Still, it's no accident that Ronald Reagan was into astrology and extraterrestrials, both of which are phantasmal glosses for manipulating the present. It's also not an accident that it is only at the end of his tenure that we were told of his incapacity to handle his responsibilities. Like Nixon and Carter before him, he mirrors the world-planning apparatus of his time. That apparatus has now completely and hysterically committed itself and the future to

"Yes," he said. "Quite. And of course I needn't add that touring is not recreation for the human soul. Its ability to move at all is a recent one. Three hundred years ago human souls had no such capacity. But like any other aspect of consciousness it evolves to meet new conditions. During the tribal migrations of prehistory, for instance, the migrants lived for generations without souls. That accounts in part for the extraordinary brutality of the migrations. Fifty miles from home and a man was a barbarian."

A tall, good-looking man about my age sidled up to the bar and dropped his overnight bag at his feet. There was something familiar about him, but I couldn't quite place it. He was dressed in blue jeans and a weathered brown leather jacket, and was flipping an American Express card between his thumb and forefinger. Then it came to me: this was an Akron Design Center Visigoth. He looked even more exhausted and disoriented than I'd been feeling, but somehow I couldn't feel sorry for him.

My companion noticed my distraction and followed my gaze. "You shouldn't feel sympathy. He's one of those that deliberately gave up his soul."

"Look," I said. "All day I've had this sense that I might at any moment go spinning off my axis. Does this have anything to do with the temporary separation from my soul?"

---

miracles, be it nuclear fusion, artificial intelligence, biotechnology, Jehovah, or little green men in spaceships. It is hoping one or more of those are going to come through—to supervene and save our fat asses. And while it is hoping for it, R & D funding is being cut across the board to maintain present gravy levels.

Another choice does exist. It is much less dramatic, and immensely difficult. We can learn to examine our operational logic in a systematic way, and to examine the limitations of its logical processes and unexamined premises. No human society has suc-

THE DIFFERENCE BETWEEN HUMAN AND OTHER SYSTEMS

"Definitely," he answered, shifting back to the computer-tech gloss. "Most of your physical and emotional interface nodes—the points that process incoming data—are unavailable to you because they're created and maintained by your soul. You're relying on ego and stored intellectual fuel to keep you balanced right now. That's why the longer you travel, the more likely you are to commit purely selfish acts, or to make decisions on a purely abstract basis. Or other kinds of stupid behaviors I needn't spell out for you. There's nothing mystical about any of this. It's coldly pragmatic."

"You're suggesting that the soul is an inherent containment technology that operates in typical fashion, right? And that there are possible strategies for nurturing the soul—mine or anyone else's?"

"Yes. It's very simple. Travel as little as you can, for one. And never travel for purposes of avoiding the kinds of issues the soul is intended to help you with."

"Huh?"

"One of the singularly evil practices consumerism supports is the practice of traveling to exotic destinations in order to avoid the reality of everyday living. Most people do that precisely at the point where they should begin to investigate the particularities around them. And those pleasure ghettos are the worst. Two

---

cessfully done this. But then no human society has had our overwhelmingly urgent need to do so.

This is the context of Public Eye's case: it is in history, but not circumscribed by the intellectual and methodological restrictions of conventional historiography. It is psychogenetic, but psychological analysis is highly unlikely to offer solutions because psychology has become regulatory to the existing political control structures. As the Akron Design Center finds more and more entertaining (and unavoidable) ways for us as individuals to have

weeks at Club Med will kill a weak human soul, or preempt an incipient one. That's a far greater danger than herpes, which is what most people who go to those places worry about."

"I think most of them already have herpes, actually."

That got the smallest trace of a smile, but not for long. "That's your joke. I have no precise data on that question. As a matter of fact," he said, finishing his soda water and getting to his feet. "I'm pretty well out of relevant information."

I half-expected him to vanish. I even closed my eyes to see if he would. "It's been, er, a slice," I said.

"No it hasn't," he said. "This is not a mystical experience. Everything I've told you can be secured by evidence. It's a question of accurate processing. I've merely offered you the metaphoric software."

"Whatever you say."

I closed my eyes again, feeling weary and disoriented. When I opened them, the Akron Design Center Visigoth at the bar was gone. In his place was the old man I'd been talking to, dressed in the Visigoth's clothes. He was flipping the AmEx card, looking around the bar for someone else to hit on.

I had a plane to catch. And trudging along in the cool evening somewhere in the middle of Pennsylvania, I had a soul to placate. Or, for the first time in my life, a soul to disbelieve in.

---

a nice day, the number of days left for us as a species diminishes in ratio.

Public Eye's elusive case is not up for conventional solution—meaning that it is not going to go away if the perpetrators of evil are caught and punished, the victims identified, and restitution made. Public Eye can't go back to an apartment high above the city to drink scotch, play sentimental music, and work out an existential score-sheet. No one will ever again be able to do that in good conscience.

THE DIFFERENCE BETWEEN HUMAN AND OTHER SYSTEMS

AKRON DESIGN CENTER ANTIDOTES
Tourism

Tourism is a form of social idiocy, and must be subject to educational remedies.

a: Tourists traveling beyond a radius of five hundred miles must pass exams prior to departure on the cultural, social, and political history of their destination, and must provide a short explanation of what it is they are avoiding in their local environment by touring.

b: Tourists traveling to Third World countries must provide detailed analyses of comparative GNP and individual annual incomes, along with a list of at least five reasons why citizens in destination countries have reason to resent the presence of tourists.

c: All corporate or private holdings in international tourist facilities must be sold to citizens of said country.

d: Tourism brochures will be designated as a special target for TIA intervention

---

BUREAUCRATIC, CORPORATE, AND OTHER BODIES OF LOGIC

Since the time of Heraclitus most political theory and practice have been grounded on a distinction between individual consciousness and collective reality—the private body alienated from the body of society and/or nature, but connected to the social body by the common need to avoid violence. Almost all

131

VICTIMS OF NOTHING AT ALL

There's this little café I sometimes go to when I need a radical shift in ambience. It's called La Cocina, and if you live in a city of any size, you can probably find one like it: feminist, leftist, and oriented distinctively south of the border. The one I'm talking about is run as a cooperative, with the profits going to organizations that help abused women on welfare, or refugees from politically violent countries in South and Central America. Most of the workers are women, and roughly half of those are Latin American, the others, feminists.

The walls of the café are covered with feminist slogans and large handmade posters outlining conditions in different Central and South American dictatorships: population and geographical details, child mortality rates, illiteracy rates, and so forth. On the posters are badly collaged photographs of pregnant women, unhappy children, and males in a variety of military postures:

---

the theory and practice can be philosophically and administratively resolved in a theoretical paradigm that was developed most thoroughly during the Middle Ages. This paradigm proposes that political rulers, or authorities—mostly kings in those days—have two bodies.

One of the two bodies is a corporeal body of functional authority, be it king, pod of generals, crazed dictator, revolutionary vanguard, or our own "democratically" elected governments of lawyers and business leaders. The theoretical purpose and mandate of this functional body are the control, maintenance, and

BUREAUCRATIC, CORPORATE, AND OTHER BODIES OF LOGIC

aggressive if holding American-made weapons, defensive if carrying identifiably Eastern-bloc-manufactured arms. The place has as exact a theogonic iconography as you'd find in a dentist's office or an evangelist's tabernacle. Kill Plaque. Kill Sinners. Kill Imperialists.

None of the slogans openly suggest killing men, but most of the feminists who work there give the impression that they regard men and imperialists pretty much as one and the same. Men are tolerated in La Cocina, but they aren't welcome unless they're what I call "frizzies"—guys who wear hiking boots, straggly beards, and heavy, home-knit sweaters. That doesn't exactly describe my personal style, so they don't approve of me. But because I'm quiet and reasonably polite unless provoked, the feminists treat me with a disdainful civility. Since they're running a business they don't go out of their way to look for trouble, but they're clearly suspicious that I might harbor charge cards and sexist attitudes.

I go there because they serve me my coffee and then ignore me. It's exactly what I want out of a café. Mild hostility toward my downwardly mobile white middle-class heterosexual male persona makes me feel absolutely at home. It's what I get, more covertly and thus less comfortingly, from the mainstream of my culture. The difference, of course, is that in those mainstream

---

well-being of the other body—the body politic of enfranchised citizens, along with their customs and their material wealth. Across history different corporeal authorities have obviously held different emphases on control, conservation, and well-being of the body politic, and each has defined those three terms—and the structure of the body politic—in a characteristic way.

But as material wealth has grown, and socioeconomic infrastructure has grown with it, the energies of authority have shifted with increasing rapidity from social control to conservation to engendering well-being. These shifts have created a third and

133

currents I'm suspected of being a failure. At La Cocina they're suspicious I might not be.

Most of the time, I can spend a four-hour stretch there without either prospect or danger of being disturbed. No waiters with names like Brad or Bruce introduce themselves or ass-kiss for tips, no Sarahs or Stacys worry over whether I'm Jack the Ripper, Prince Charming, or an opportunity to display their sensibility or good taste. La Cocina isn't for everyone, but I'm the sort who'll take polite hostility over impersonal friendliness any day of the week. This may seem like a very small mercy to you, but I'm deeply grateful that no one in La Cocina has ever counseled me to have a nice day.

Ironically, the only person who's ever struck up a conversation with me while I'm at La Cocina is an old friend who happens to be named Brad. He's really not a true "Brad"—he wears no name tag, no career path is being projected, he has taken no second-year university commerce courses to upgrade his curriculum vitae. There's nothing Brad about Brad at all, come to think of it.

He's not really a friend, either. He's an "old" friend, which means that we used to be close and aren't now. He's a frizzy, in his late thirties. On the peculiar fashion and accessory set of La Cocina he could be mistaken for a piece of furniture. That's what

---

largely unrecognized political body—the body of physical and procedural infrastructure that rises from and enjoins the activities of the other two. Until recently that has been experienced chiefly as bureaucracy. But now its conformation is changing, and we can see it for what it is: a body of logic that is capable of engendering independent authority.

In the nineteenth century and through to the middle of the twentieth, bureaucracy gathered unique powers to itself. Mostly those powers lent themselves to political and social reaction: the steamroller logic of petrified procedure, apparently inscrutable

he goes to La Cocina for, I suspect. He likes being a piece of furniture. Except, unfortunately, around me. Every time I see him there we get into an argument.

Now, an argument with Brad is never a formal exchange of discursive information and opinion. It's more like having a phalanx of conservative radicalisms attach themselves to your ankle and hang on no matter how vigorously you shake or kick.

Conservative radicals are those people who were fashionable in the mid-1970s, when people still thought that capitalism was about to collapse. Don't confuse conservative radicals with radical conservatives, who are fashionable right now, and believe that the capitalist system is so sturdy and virtuous it ought to at very least regress back to the economic practices and attitudes of the 1920s, and the political ones of the 1950s.

Lieutenant Colonel Oliver North, for instance, is a radical conservative. That means he wears his hair short, has homosexual fantasies about General Eisenhower, wants to kill Commies— and feels that it is a service to God and the American Way of Life that he and like-minded associates should get rich doing it. Brad doesn't approve of Oliver North, or anything else that isn't firmly within the conservative radical mind-set—including me, of course.

"North," he announces, "is a sexist asshole."

---

and relentlessly narrow protocols, and a fundamental intolerance for new ideas—a kind of societal reptilian cortex. In these respects it differs little from the religious bureaucracies of the Middle Ages. The uniqueness derives from its vast scale, from its marriage to mass-production technology, and from its capacity for generating social terror from normality and routine—Franz Kafka's nightmare.

Bureaucracy has also developed a reactionary mission that resembles that of organic life: to grow larger and stronger, and to preserve existing procedures and forms of behavior, however

"What's sexism got to do with it?" I snap back. "This was a guy bent on a lot more than mistreating women. He subverted the American Constitution."

"What about the way he treated Fawn Hall?" Brad insists, peering intently down his tunnel. "Wasn't she a victim of his sexism?"

Let me pretend to jog your memory while I take a few shots at these people. Fawn Hall, please recall, North's executive secretary, was and is the prototype radical conservative bimbo. Out of loyalty to North and no one is quite sure what else, she was also pretty abusive to the Constitution, deliberately destroying government documents to help North cover up his activities. Like North and John Poindexter, she probably lied in front of the U.S. Congress.

Unlike her mentors, Fawn Hall helped her career doing all this. Now she hosts corporate-sponsored television specials and fields daily offers from *Playboy* and *Penthouse,* who want her to show them (and us) her tits.

I'm feeling mischievous with Brad. "I'd bet money North wasn't boinking her," I tell him. "She and North probably treated each other like Perry Mason and Della Street. Or like Ken and Barbie. I'd bet money that none of them has genitals at all."

---

counterproductive and self-defeating, against dynamic or organic intrusion. Yet the astonishing influxes of material wealth and a parallel growth in population and the variety of commodities have kept all but a few from recognizing in bureaucracy the subtle reflexes of life-form evolution.

By the 1950s bureaucracy was effectively synonymous with the public sector of our political and social economy. It had subsumed much of the policy-making functions that were previously the province of direct political authority—elected or otherwise—by the physical extensions of its logical processes. I

Brad doesn't bite. "So what?" he sneers. "They're Enemies of the People. And the Revolution."

That's the conservative radical response I was expecting.

"Which *people* are you talking about," I ask him, refusing to go along with his rhetorical use of the upper case. "And what Revolution? Far as I can see, there's no revolution going on around here for them to be the enemies of. And if you mean that North and Hall are part of a semiclandestine American program to overthrow the government of Nicaragua, well, I can only agree to a point. They were so incompetent they might as well have been working for the KGB. And I'll thank you to remember that *all* the governments involved are authoritarian. In their different ways, they're each more interested in asserting their authority than in fondling your private abstractions."

I know that such remarks will infuriate him, and right on cue, he loses it, blows up, and walks out of the café in a huff. Fine with me. I get to go back to the book I'm reading.

But as I watch him leave I start to feel sorry for him, and slightly puzzled, as always, at the way he insists on reducing reality to a string of slogans. He's not a stupid man. It's just that the way his life has gone has damaged his sensors so much he has to employ a belief system in order to sort incoming phenomena— his mind only operates deductively. Fifty years ago he'd have been

---

can cite areas where this has occurred until we are all nauseous with fear and loathing, and so, probably, can you. The lunatic extension of our doomsday military system is perhaps the most dramatic example. But other illustrations, like the growth of automotive freeways in the United States during the post–World War II era should be equally convincing and more visible.

It isn't all lunatic, of course. Some of it has been pretty intelligent and humane. Despite all-too-frequent episodes of authoritarian brutality and the streamlining of methods for suppressing dissent, modern bureaucracy has also allowed the industrialized

a priest—or a police officer. He'd have been much happier with either identity.

When I first met him, in the 1960s, we were both trying to figure out how to be poets, gulping up the touchy-feely cosmological rhetoric of those years. We wrote poetry based wholly on our feelings about what we were and weren't getting from the political and social systems—and any females who accidentally or deliberately penetrated our self-absorption. When that perceptual technique collapsed beneath us, its sweaty-sweet body music drowned out by the howls of the coyotes and wolves that swooped in to devour the effete wealth-induced innocence that engendered it, Brad discovered the New Left. He rode that half-Marxist, half-Freudian libertarian mule deeper and deeper into delusional reality, first via a nervous breakdown and then straight into a Marxist study group. He prostrated himself before the diamat, and wholeheartedly joined the group in bashing the shit out of any ideological rivals found competing in the search for the Correct Revolutionary Line.

It's only blind luck that a Jim Jones or a Charlie Manson didn't get to him. And thank God he isn't an Iranian or a Cambodian. We know what happens to frustrated poets who end up as priests or police officers in those countries.

In the early 1980s he settled into a male support group for a

---

nations to distribute wealth and social services more widely (if not more equitably) than ever before. In those same nations it has nourished and administered a legal infrastructure that has achieved a relative degree of social justice, or at least offers the apparatus to those resourceful enough to use it. As we know, it has also gotten more subtle at terrorizing and humiliating undocile citizens, and it has managed to impose, by promising the disadvantaged nations the same levels of wealth achieved by the industrialized world, its conceptual apparatus and its procedural values on nearly the entire planet.

BUREAUCRATIC, CORPORATE, AND OTHER BODIES OF LOGIC

radical feminist organization called "Rape Control." The cell he joined was controlled by a woman named Ellen Crowley, a covert alcoholic ten years his senior. Ellen fancied herself a cross between Emma Goldman and Amelia Earhart, except that she was too lazy to read Marx, and the only thing she flew was forty-ounce bottles of cheap vodka. She had the personality and interpersonal tactics of Valerie Solonas, the founder of SCUM—the Society for Cutting Up Men. Brad fell in love with her instantly, and the two of them ended up living together, sort of.

The "sort of" was that Ellen sent him off to a government hydroelectric project to work for the movement—meaning that he stayed a long distance away from her and sent his paychecks to her in the mail. Whenever he was allowed to visit her in the city, which wasn't often, she subjected him to "criticism sessions" in which she read his private diaries to her group. The diaries, in the sexually deprived environment that is standard fare in construction camps, were filled with chicken-choking reveries. They were also excellent grist for Ellen's radical feminist mill.

Eventually, Ellen lost interest in radical feminism and went off to live on some island with a scientologist who ran a scam that involved manufacturing consciousness-raising hardware—stained-glass pyramids and other junk—for the human potential industry. He was using a group of weak-willed idiots stupid

---

The only practical limits to the totalization of bureaucratic power that have emerged have been unexpected ones. The main limit seems to be related to size and technology. All technologically dense infrastructure has an embedded algorithm—or operating system—that generates value and eventually is powerful enough to dictate the private and career values of its operators. The most dramatic example is the U.S. military, but practically every major institution and infrastructure component in contemporary Western societies seeks to universalize its algorithm and logic beyond the specific context to which it pertains. It's called

enough to work for nothing but his brand of enlightenment, and Ellen moved in to help him rule his ersatz kingdom.

For a while she neglected to mention her new domestic arrangement to Brad, who continued to labor diligently for the movement up at the hydroelectric project. He kept on sending his paychecks to her, and she used them to stockpile materials for her new boyfriend's pyramids.

When Brad discovered what was going on he stopped sending his paychecks and dropped out of the movement. The experience left him broke, emotionally wrecked, and confused over whether the guilt he felt about women derived from the way they're treated or because of the things he thought about them in the trashed privacy of his own mind. The criticism sessions left him with the physical demeanor of someone who fears he might at any moment step on his own testicles—or be forced to by someone else.

Somehow, he got a job in the city, rented a small apartment, and began to hang out at La Cocina, phoning his old friends from time to time for conversation and company, greeting them with a confusing mélange of rhetoric drawn from his last half-dozen identities.

So it's Tuesday afternoon in La Cocina, a few weeks after the Oliver North argument. I was drinking a cappuccino and reading

---

interagency imperialism, and many of us have firsthand experience of it by now. Those who work in the medical, transportation, corrections, security, and design/planning fields (to name only some) should recognize the rhetorical élans that compete for professional dignity, political control, and budgets with other infrastructure components. Understanding their ultimate consequences is a lot trickier and more frightening.

The other current limit to bureaucracy—probably now a temporary one—is the physical boundaries of nations. As infrastructure component systems grow, particularly in the field of

BUREAUCRATIC, CORPORATE, AND OTHER BODIES OF LOGIC

the newspaper when Brad shambled in. He spotted me immediately, and headed for my table, obviously having forgotten our
hassle over Oliver North. As I watched him approach I realized
that his broken-spirited gait probably had the opposite effect
from the one he intends it to have. It made him appear more
intensely male—bearlike, almost, as if his legs were heavier than
the rest of his body.

"So," I said as he eased himself into the chair across from me,
"how're things?"

Brad has never had the slightest reserve about belaboring his
friends with his troubles, and today is no different. He launched
directly into his current personal nightmare.

"Oh, it's pretty awful. I've been wrestling with some *very* heavy
stuff lately."

I was only half-paying attention, and I made the error of asking
him what it was.

"I'm really getting into figuring out why I let Ellen put me
through all that stuff."

"You may have let her do it, but she was the one who actually
did the deeds," I pointed out. "It might be more productive to
get mad as hell at her and make sure no one else does it to
you again."

"Oh, I deserved it," he said.

---

economics, they've tended to attempt to impose standards and
practices across the arbitrary physical boundaries of national
states and languages. So far these tendencies have met with
mixed success. On political terms they've met with very little
success. The dynamics of ideological nationalism blind-sides
them with problems of differing custom, scale, and context.

For instance, the major military bureaucracies in the world,
Russian, American, and Chinese, operate on very large but still
national scales, even though their arenas of activity are often
much wider. The Vietnam War dramatically demonstrated that

"Aw bullshit," I scoffed. "No one *deserves* to be mistreated. No one. Stop being a professional victim."

"Well, I am a victim. But I'm also a victimizer."

"Of whom?" I demanded irritably. The sympathy I felt for him when he walked in was evaporating fast.

"Oh, I participated. I always participate. And because I'm a male, I'm making it happen. If it wasn't Ellen it would be someone else."

I didn't point out that what he just said was a sexist remark. We'd been through that before, and I didn't want to lead him on. "I think maybe it's time you got out of your private history and into the real world."

"No. I've got to work this out."

I couldn't see why, but I let that go too. I asked him why he was a victim. His answer was shockingly simple.

"I was molested as a child," he said, almost smugly.

"You were what?"

"Molested. M-o-l-e-s-t-e-d. By my father. Surprised?"

I happen to know his father reasonably well. He's a big dumb aggressive businessman who isn't very good at business and drank himself into a series of heart attacks several years ago. The last time I saw him he was staring at walls from a wheelchair. Somehow, I just couldn't see him molesting Brad. The only kinky

---

the military and political apparatus of one nation can no longer be efficiently imposed on another. At first, the United States' humiliating experience in Southeast Asia appeared to demonstrate merely the invulnerable virtue of Marxist ideology and organizational logic. But the subsequent invasion and occupation of Cambodia by Vietnam, which have resulted in Vietnam's "Vietnam," and the Soviet military's woeful failure to suppress religion-based self-determination in Afghanistan exposed the same failure of Marxist systems.

If I appear to be arguing that we're safe from a totalized bureau-

thing I can recall about him is that he kept running for political office and losing. Year after year. But because this is a world in which every one of us is a potential molester, I withheld my skepticism.

"Molested exactly how?" I asked. "Do you mean that your Old Man bullied you when you were a kid, or beat on you, or that he actually got down and fucked you?"

Brad grimaced. "Don't be gross," he said. "And anyway, I'm not sure. My therapist and I are still in the process of coming to grips with it."

I gazed around the room, suddenly wondering why, in the mid-1980s, I was in this particular place listening to this particular man. The scenery provided no answers. The café's sound system was playing South American folk songs, which I couldn't understand partly because the volume was Muzak level and partly because the songs were in Spanish and I don't know the language.

Two women, South Americans, were trotting in and out of the men's washroom. Something in there was broken and they were deciding that it was unfixable and would have to be abandoned. One of them went to the counter, probably to ask for materials to make an OUT OF ORDER sign, and ran afoul of the Feminist operating the cappuccino machine.

---

cracy because of the increased firepower of hand-held weapons, well, don't relax yet. All that's required is an erasure of the local frame of reference and scale, and a retooling of system logic on a planetary basis, activity sector by activity sector. And that is precisely what is occurring.

Let's back up some, and examine the theoretical ground on which current infrastructure is built and operates. The goals of national systems of bureaucracy are value-based in definite—if rarely examined—assumptions about what constitutes Good and Evil. In modern capitalist democracies, Good has tended to

With a show of pedagogic certitude, the Feminist marched to
the washroom with the two South American women cowering in
her wake, and stood in the doorway with her hands on her hips.

She stayed in that posture for quite a while, long enough for
me to realize that Brad and I were being treated to a kind of
contemporary morality play. From the Feminist's point of perception, this was no doubt a confrontation with two unpleasantly
troubling phenomena: a repository of male filth, and a technological breakdown generally reserved for males to fix.

It had her paralyzed. She didn't want to go inside the washroom in the first place, and she certainly didn't want to have to
touch a toilet that had been used by men. It was apparent that
she didn't know how to fix it, but getting a male to fix it was
politically incorrect. The only other solution was to stand there
and will the toilet to fix itself.

Meanwhile, the uncooperative toilet was screwing up with
real enthusiasm. Water was beginning to pool in the doorway,
and I could now detect splashing and gurgling sounds under the
South American folk Muzak.

Now, if I'd been almost anywhere else, I would have gotten off
my duff and asked if there was anything I could do to help. But
this was La Cocina. If I'd stuck my nose into this one, I'd likely
have gotten stabbed in the throat for being an overbearing sexist

focus on a shifting balance between litigative social justice and
equality of economic opportunity for the individual, and at the
public level, a scattered (and less successful) pursuit of com-
monwealth—improved health and welfare, universal literacy
and excellence in scholarship, theoretical science, and applied
technology.

In the Marxist democracies, Good gets defined as equality of
social services and the leveling of hereditary or class-based economic advantages, mostly at the expense of individual liberty and
initiative. In the disadvantaged parts of the world, Good for the

prick. At very least I would have been scowled out of the place permanently for attempting to undermine the authority of the woman in charge, who I knew damned well believed it was more important to teach her two South American women that they don't need any macho assholes with gold chains around their necks to make the world function properly. I don't own any gold chains, but that wouldn't have mattered.

Luckily, I had an alternative sitting right across the table from me. "Brad," I said. "Maybe you'd better help that woman."

He turned around to look, but stayed firmly in his chair. "No way," he said. "She's in Rape Control. She'd probably stab me in the throat."

"Well, I can't help her, either."

He nodded. "Maybe the toilet'll stop on its own after a while," he said, as if he thought her political will might actually do the job.

Now, as you probably recognize, there is no political will on this planet that can fix a leaking toilet. I'm not making fun of the women of La Cocina when I say this, either. That afternoon I sincerely wished their political will *could* fix toilets, because eventually the water ran across the floor, under and past the table Brad and I were sitting at, past the silk-screened political posters from Nicaragua, and into a flush-mounted electrical outlet someone had thoughtfully installed in the floor.

---

wealthy classes has become the power to control the poor, and recently, the power to consume in the manner and scale of the privileged classes in the West. For the poor, Good continues to be what it has always been: adequate food and shelter.

Evil has had a more stable character: it has been stupidity, ignorance, lack of material resources, human cruelty, and perversity—all the things that are parasitic to the dynamic and irregular pursuit of the Good, however that has been defined.

I'm speaking in dangerously abstract terms, I realize. Yet in an information-governed society and culture based on liberal demo-

145

There were several loud pops from the outlet and most of the lights went out. I heard someone yelling and some doors slamming. A minute or two later the rest of the lights went out, and the noise from the toilet eased. La Cocina was abruptly dark and silent.

This was not the right time to leave. "More asshole males disappearing at the first sign of difficulty" would have been the verdict. So Brad and I sat there in semidarkness, listening to the Feminist and the South American women slish-slosh through the puddles of water without being able to make a decision as to who should (another situationally tricky word here) man the mops.

Brad was determined to continue our conversation. "So where were we?" he demanded.

"Baseball," I lied. "We were discussing the baseball scores."

It was a few seconds before he caught on. "No we weren't," he replied firmly. "I don't follow baseball. We were talking about . . ."

He trailed off. "Your problems," I said. "With Ellen. And with your father, I guess."

"Yeah. Listen. It's all true. That's what's been tormenting me for years. Since I was a kid."

"I thought you just discovered that it happened."

---

cratic values, it's become very easy to define Good and Evil on pragmatic terms. What is Good is that which affords citizens—collectively or individually—autonomous, informed consciousness of self, others, and environment, and provides them with the material and intellectual tools to protect and enhance that consciousness. Evil is that which impedes such consciousness.

So, obviously, Evil is winning. Why?

Well, we know the answers for the Third World, where the key issues remain those of subsistence, not citizenship. We also know the answers for the Marxist world, where, despite glimmerings of

"Well, it was always there, according to my therapist, and I was trying to remember, subconsciously. That's why I was the way I was. I mean, it explains a lot of my problems."

I was having a mighty hard time concentrating on his problems. The practical ones around me, with the overflowing toilet and the short-circuited electrical system and the temporarily short-circuited women were just too immediate. Besides that, even in the gloom I could see that a medium-sized turd riddled with bits of undigested corn had escaped the overflowing toilet intact. As a matter of fact, it was edging its way toward our table on the flood. Worse, I could also foresee that Brad was probably going to tromp on it when it arrived under our table.

I did what I've been trained to do in moments of intellectual extremity—I quoted somebody else. I quoted several people, actually. "People are what they do" (André Malraux). "Suffering gives no rights" (Albert Camus).

The turd was now beneath his left foot, which was jangling nervously just above the floor.

"Look at it this way, Brad," I said, hoping to stun him with my erudition and thus arrest his nervous foot long enough for the turd to float past and beyond. "It's time you let go of your private agonies. You're an adult, and sooner or later you've got to abandon

---

structural change, information remains trapped by orthodoxies that are so counterproductive and repressive that the political and economic systems there seem likely to collapse soon from the weight of their accumulated entropy.

For us in the West, the answer may not be so apparent, particularly where the system has us all spinning so fast we're too dizzy to ask the question. We have an information-manipulating economy superseding a bureaucratic culture or—more precisely still—merging and interbreeding with it. The offspring of this merger fill our communications channels, our multina-

your parents—take away their power over you—and take control
of your life. And take control of your imagination."

The last word was a mistake. His foot came down hard, right
onto the turd, which had paused there, as if to listen to my
speech.

"You can't control imagination," he said, as a distinct fecal
miasma filled the air around us. He looked down at the floor
and groaned. "Aw, shit!" he yelled as he realized what he'd done.
Then, to make it worse, he sloshed his shoe in the water, trying
to free it of the offending substance. The miasma grew thicker.

One of the South American women was watching Brad's an-
tics, but she merely curled her lip and walked away. God knows
what she was thinking. Corn-eating men, probably.

"Sure men are disgusting," I wanted to shout at her, "shitting
on the floor at the slightest opportunity. But this turd isn't ours."

Maybe Brad's disease was contagious. I felt distinctly responsible *anyway*. I'm male, after all, and I have fired guns and eaten
corn: guilt by association.

"There are thousands of things in the environment that manipulate imagination," I said, trying to recall when I last ate
corn. "Why are you so reluctant to tamper with your own?"

"Imagination is sacred," he answered. "Jesus, what a stench."

"Nothing is sacred," I replied, covering my nose with my hand

---

tional corporate boardrooms, and our educational institutions.

When we look at the basic values that are supposed to be
generating social and physical support infrastructure for Western
societies, the first place to look (even if those of us who are non-
Americans don't like to) is the U.S. Constitution. This document
undertakes to guarantee Americans the right to life (read "relative
subsistence and public safety"), liberty (read "freedom of political
choice and expression"), and the pursuit of happiness (I won't
even try to interpret what that has come to mean). An interpreta-

in the dim hope it might forfend the stink. "Your parents tampered with your imagination, and so did Ellen. Every major consumer corporation in the world is looking to tamper with it. And most of them are succeeding. La Cocina is even tampering with your mind."

"What?" Brad demanded. "Take your hand away from your mouth. You're mumbling and I can't hear you."

I repeated my last sentence, loudly exhaling as I spoke.

He looked around the room as if searching for the evidence, and found the Feminist with the political will advancing on us through the gloom with a mop and bucket.

"Move, will you?" she said sourly. "I'd like to clean up this disgusting mess."

The way she leaned on the last word made it clear she believed the turd was ours, that we'd deliberately sabotaged the toilet after depositing the turd in it, or that we'd taken her disaster as an opportunity to defecate on the floor. No limits to the crudity and cruelty of men. She stood over us while I packed up my briefcase, looking as if she were deliberating over which of us was the culprit.

I turned my back to her and moved to a table near the back of the café. Brad shuffled after me. I caught myself wondering whether I should tell her I haven't eaten corn lately. No, I

---

tion of that document that nearly everyone will agree with (in public, anyway) would run roughly as follows: *The state has a moral responsibility to ensure that national wealth and power are distributed justly, and that opportunities—for education, access to social services, and for the accumulation of private wealth, spiritual and bodily experiences—are available on an equitable basis.*

So far so good. And until just recently nearly everyone would have agreed with this one as well: *In a just economic order, the needs of the poor should take priority over the wants of the rich.*

decided, that wouldn't work. Confessions of innocence from the enemy are perceived as admissions of guilt.

We sat down at a table near a window. I lit up a cigarette and idly considered turning Brad in. "Hey, lady, he ate corn last night. I saw him!"

"Hey!" hollered the Feminist. "Yeah, you! That's the no smoking section!"

I stubbed out the cigarette and turned to Brad. He was watching the Feminist intently, looking utterly guilty of whatever horrible behavior she cared to imagine for him.

"It wasn't you," I said gently. "You didn't jam the toilet, and the turd wasn't yours."

"Well, it could have been."

"Sure," I replied. "It could have been that woman's too. Feminists shit, you know. She could have set up the whole thing just to bully us. Or it could have been one of those Central American women who couldn't read the sign on the door."

"No feminist would do *that*," he said, ignoring the other possibility even though it was more plausible.

"Well, probably not," I admitted. "Not this way, anyhow. Sometimes things just happen, and people see them inaccurately. Or maybe they see things in ways that support only what they want to see. Sort of to narrow the interpretative threshold."

Now, in an increasing number of Western countries, there will be loud shouts that the state should keep its interfering ass out of the nation's boardrooms.

This one is now thoroughly contentious: *Individual and community rights to dignified and meaningful work, along with the rights of any given geographical and political community to have at least a reasonable participation in controlling modes of production, should take priority over the right to maximize profits and to accumulate and disperse capital.*

No fucking way on that one, right? We've now got a world

"Huh? What threshold?" he stammered. "She wouldn't . . ."

"Well," I said, "maybe she did and maybe she didn't. But someone's guilty. I think she knows it was you but she doesn't want to blame you because you go so well with her accessories."

"Pardon me?" he asked, completely flustered now. "Did you say 'accessories'?"

"Yeah. Accessories. Pearls and black sweaters and makeup."

"Feminists don't wear makeup. They're not in the world to please men anymore, you know."

"Oh, lighten up and listen. That's not what I mean."

He sensed a small advantage, and dived for it. "Well, I wish you'd be a little more explicit. You're always talking in riddles."

"Okay," I said. "I'll be explicit. Everybody does fashion and accessories now. Not just rich people and yuppies. Mafia hit men are all screwed up on fashion and accessories, Feminists are. So are you.

"Do you remember Zorba the Greek, years ago when we were in university? It started off with the book, and then there was the movie, with Anthony Quinn and Alan what's his name."

Brad looked uncomfortable. "Yeah, sure. Vaguely."

"Do you recall there's a scene in the movie where the English guy—Alan Bates, that's right—asks Anthony Quinn to teach him to dance? So Quinn shows him how to do it, and Bates

---

economy, and any impedance of the flow of profits and capital movement by the state is a declaration of intent to commit economic or political suicide. Look at what was done to the Allende government in Chile in 1973 if you want an extreme example. But more pertinent examples can be found by checking out your municipal, state/provincial, and national governments, all of which now act as meek servants of the corporate sector, not of their citizens. Citizens are regarded chiefly as clients or potential clients clamoring for services.

Tracing how Western societies got to this state of affairs isn't any

dances, sort of, awkwardly at first, and then as the music gets louder, he gets better and better until the two of them are dancing up a storm. To a full symphony orchestra that only we can hear."

"What orchestra?"

"The one on the movie sound track. We could hear it, because it was part of the movie, but they couldn't because they were in the movie. They were standing on some hill in Greece, so how could they? But we can. You can only hear movie music if you're in a movie theater. Or at least that's the way it used to be."

"What's your point?" he said irritably.

"Well, think about what happened to us after that. First of all, we left the theater humming that tune, right? Then we went out and bought the record. Then a few days later, outside that old motel cabin I was living in the two of us tried to do the Zorba dance on that big log that served as a curb? I had the stereo speakers stuck out on the front porch so we could tell the whole neighborhood who we really were and what we could do."

Brad suddenly giggled. "Yeah, I remember how you fell off the log and sprained your ankle."

I'd forgotten that part. It'd hurt like hell. And suddenly sitting in La Cocina nearly twenty years later, I had a vivid memory of lying on my backside next to the log clutching my ankle and

---

easier than following its logic. The more or less universal adoption of the corporate planning model by Western governments during the 1960s, which created a standard model for competition between public sector agencies, was the most visible signal that fundamental changes were occurring. Few spotted the changes, and still fewer recognized the implications of the corporate planning model. For nearly three decades state agencies with narrow corporate goals have been busily defining, exploiting, and widening "market niches" exactly the same way as Kellogg's has been working the breakfast cereal market. And as the decades

BUREAUCRATIC, CORPORATE, AND OTHER BODIES OF LOGIC

shouting at Brad. I wasn't shouting at him to help me. I was trying to get him to shut the goddamned music off.

"Forget that I got hurt," I said. "That wasn't the point. What happened next?"

"What do you mean, what happened next? In the next half hour or the next week or month or year? I don't get it."

"I mean, what happened to Zorba the Greek."

"There was no such person," he said, "so nothing happened to him."

"Wrong! Six months later you could hear his music in every supermarket in North America, except that now it was all mellow-stringed and mushy, as if Zorba had immigrated to the United States and had gotten fat and was living in a condominium development for old folks, so he's Zorba the Alzheimer's or Zorba the SuperShopper, or whatever will sell merchandise and force you to have a nice day.

"The music wasn't telling you to dance anymore. It was out there following you from place to place, whispering at you to buy, to push your cart down the aisle and fill it full of groceries and head for the drugstore next door."

Brad was gazing at the Feminist and her Latin American assistants. "Get to the point," he said.

"The point is that nowadays nothing gets through to individual

---

have passed, the concept of *public service* has atrophied. It has been replaced by mission- and project-oriented functionaries as much interested in aggrandizing their share of public funding as in creating rational and just systems of public fulfillment.

This may not seem so bad, but it is undermining the principle of universal solidarity on which Western democracies are supposed to be based. We're being reduced to self-interested tribal enclaves attempting to colonialize, subjugate, or control others, and we're increasingly under the control of a limited number of political and economic algorithms that ensure solidarity only

memory without it getting retooled into some kind of commercial control mechanism. It's gotten to everything—sex, politics, everything about the way we live."

"Well, I don't see what this has to do with my problems," he said, his glance flicking back and forth from me to the Feminist.

"The point is you should only trust first-generation media. Everything else is wired solid, including your problems."

I wasn't quite getting through to him, but I had the feeling that if I could just get the right angle on Zorba the Greek, I could make him see what I was talking about. I was silently searching my brain for the right piece of information when the lights came on again, and the tape machine schlupped Latin American folk song across the room until the tape motor reached playing speed.

Things seemed ready to return to normal until the Feminist sent another wave of murky water into the floor socket with her mop. The socket sprayed an arc of sparks and popped noisily, and the folk music and lights stuttered out once again.

This time she completely lost her cool, tossing the mop into a corner and kicking over the pail. "Goddamned fucking assholes!" she shouted, and stomped behind the counter holding her face in her hands.

I thought Brad might dive under the table, but he didn't. The

---

with de-ethicized consumerisms. The cultural and spiritual nirvana offered up bears a stunning resemblance to Disney World. But when its propaganda and rhetoric are stripped away, it becomes visible as the corporate boardroom, multiplied in every direction, and the gravy of the Akron Design Center dripping from every drooling grin.

Feminist stood behind the counter, weeping, with several South American women trying to comfort her.

"You keep putting yourself into control environments," I said to him, tapping the back of his hand to pry his attention away from the Feminist. "Ellen was a control environment. And so is having your father molest you."

Brad grunted.

"So is this place," I added. "It doesn't look or sound like the pureed Zorba they ram at you when you go to the supermarket, but the effect is the same. Your screwup is that you're satisfied by the sets. You don't pay attention to the subliminal data being fed to you."

Behind the counter the Feminist was pushing away the South American women. She dried her face with a counter cloth, stepped out from behind the counter, and headed directly toward us. "She's coming over here," Brad whispered. "What do we do?"

I didn't have an answer. She might have had any of several things in mind. She might be coming to ask for our (male) help. Unlikely, but possible. At the other extreme, her mission might be one of revenge or destruction. She might, for instance, be coming to plunge a knife into Brad's throat. Or into mine. That wasn't very likely, either, but the odds were about the same as they were for her asking for help.

ARTIFICIAL INTELLIGENCE

Lurking under what I've been talking about is the thorny subject of artificial intelligence. The leading questions about artificial intelligence are not about its feasibility, or about whether it will be good or evil once it has been created. Artificial intelligence already exists, and has for some time. The questions we should be asking about it have to do with its different varieties, and with

"I'm sorry," she said, as she reached our table. "We're going to have to close for a while. I think the water has short-circuited the electricity system."

I decided to hell with the risk. "Can we help?" I asked.

She smiled. "Thanks, but no. The insurance won't allow it. You understand. But I appreciate the offer. But please come back later on, or tomorrow."

I had to pry Brad from his chair, but I got him out of there.

Out on the street, there was more than enough light for ten thousand shorted-out La Cocinas. It was real light, from the sun, and there was also the same relative silence there'd been for a few minutes at La Cocina at the height of the technofuzzout. I walked with Brad to the corner, then stopped, still thinking about how to make him see what I was talking about.

"He really did molest me," he said plaintively.

"Sure," I answered, making sure my tone of voice said the opposite. "I gotta go. Things to do."

A cloud passed over the sun just as I stepped off the curb. As I crossed the street a kid driving a muscle car with the stereo blasting out heavy metal music nearly ran me over.

Ahah! Zorba the Buddha. That'd been the name of the restaurant the Rajneeshee had opened at their commune down in

---

how to control and transform the kinds operating in our midst right now.

This is not the beginning of another of those Luddite sermons about computers à la Wendel Berry. In a sense, artificial intelligence has been an integral part of human settlements since Aristotle first harnessed the unique human impulse to classify. The variety of artificial intelligence Aristotle gave rise to is simple binary logic, the conceptual framework upon which nearly all our mass support systems are now based and on which current computer technology is wholly based.

ARTIFICIAL INTELLIGENCE

Oregon before the ridiculous Bhagwan got himself deported and his assistants started fighting over the assets just as if they were a bunch of corporate banshees, which I suppose they were once they cut the beads and colorful jumpsuits off them.

When I reached the other side of the street, still alive and now enlightened, I turned to watch Brad. He was ambling down the street with an unmistakable hop to his step. He was happy despite himself, trapped somewhere between Zorba the Greek and Zorba the Buddha, a Bhagwan truer to our civilization than the one we just sent back to India.

Another car blew past with its stereo rung up to nine. This time I had a more sobering thought. Do any of us know that what we see and feel is authentic? And we who can walk these streets in relative safety and have everything we think we desire, what *are* we to make of what we hear and see and feel, we who are the heirs to this hurricane, and victims of nothing at all?

At the simplest level, "binary" is that which pertains to, is characterized by, or compounded on two. Binary processing of an actual or theoretical situation involves digitization: reducing phenomena to discrete numerical cells of yes or no, light and dark, life and death, one or zero. In mathematics this involves positional notation of numerical properties in which value is ascribed to a digit according to its relationship to adjoining digits.

Binary logic is an extremely powerful and seductive mental tool. Reducing decision arenas to two choices, for example, has obvious appeal. As a logical system it enables the restating of all

AKRON DESIGN CENTER ANTIDOTES
Motor Vehicles

a: All automobiles of value greater than $15,000 would be required to be painted in primary industrial colors: hot pink, bright orange, electric blue, purple, and lime green. Automobiles valued in excess of $30,000 must exhibit flat Day-Glo colors: hot pink for Rolls-Royces and Jaguars, Day-Glo orange for Mercedes-Benzes and other German-manufactured vehicles, lime green for other European automobiles, and purple or blue for North American and Asian-manufactured models. All BMWs and Volvos must be equipped with lakepipes, fender skirts, and continental kits, and have the rear axle lowered so that the rear bumper of the car is within four inches of the ground.

b: Any passenger automobile with horsepower ratings in excess of 100 hp must carry a prominently displayed decal indicating the owner's name, address, marital status, and a brief sexual history that lists known dysfunctions. Any automobile with horsepower in excess of 200 hp must display a message in legible block lettering outlining just exactly what aggressive impulses the driver has stuck in his or her craw.

c: The use of cellular telephones will be prohibited in private motor vehicles for reasons of public safety and social aesthetics.

---

problems in cybernetic terms: logical extension and perpetual calculation become the system's goal, with anything that prevents extension becoming system noise to be suppressed. In binary systems, all inquiries must be unambiguous, as must be the data encoding. As Marvin Minsky points out, "the less we base our conclusions on, the fewer possibilities can exist for weakness in the arguments." This provides binary systems with an immense improvement in their ability to make very simple, repetitive calculations. The productive result is two things: improved replica-

SEVERAL TALES OF LOVE, DEATH, AND THE MISMANAGEMENT OF DANGEROUS TECHNOLOGIES

Staring up at me from the tabloid as I ate my breakfast this morning was the sober, slightly embarrassed countenance of a woman in town to publicize a new book titled *Managing Incontinence* and to give a few seminars. Accompanying the photo was a carefully tongue-in-cheek article by someone—a colleague of our friend Klein—who'd just completed an interview with the woman before the photograph was taken.

Don't get me wrong. I'm not making light of the problems of those who suffer from incontinence. As the book no doubt explains, incontinence is a legitimate medical disability (or "differ-

---

tive capacities—obvious in recent history—and an inherent and infectious syntax that tends to covertly invade nonbinary systems.

I've been using word processors for a decade as a writer, and as an urban planner, I've worked around computers longer than that. I like the things, and even if I didn't it wouldn't delude me into ignoring their pervasive presence or the impact they're having and will continue to have. They're here, and they're going to stay.

Microprocessors, the tiny data storage and transformation chips that are the core of all computers, have absolutely pene-

159

ent" ability, as the euphemism now is). It shouldn't be a target for crude jokes. There's even an international support group for those who suffer from the condition. It has fifty thousand members, and no, I'm not going to try to imagine the annual conventions they hold.

I guess I still feel, even at my age, the attraction of bathroom jokes. The attraction isn't overwhelming like it was when I was four or five years old, but some misfortunes, considered in the abstract, give me the giggles. I was born with a normal bladder, and was trained to use it appropriately. Only once, as a ten-year-old, did I mismanage my bladder. I awoke in the morning, and not wanting to spend the rest of the week sleeping on smelly sheets, I confessed all to my mother.

She didn't invite me to an Incontinence Management Seminar, and she didn't counsel me on the wide range of available professional techniques for achieving excellence in bladder management. She laughed a little, told me it was okay, and gave me two pieces of advice: take a leak before bedtime, and stay away from toilets and urinals in dreams.

Really, I'm not making fun of incontinence. I only want to criticize the way the author of *Managing Incontinence* approaches her subject. She's treating it as an entrepreneurial and professional *opportunity*. I'll bet money she's been to business school and

---

trated our everyday life. They are based on a thoroughly artificial kind of intelligence, but they're not quite what I'm talking about.

When you go to your local bank these days to withdraw cash, the intermediary between you and your money is now going to be a microprocessor. They're also in your telephone, your car, your calculator, and your alarm system. Even your toaster has them now. These new microprocessor-based appliances do things your old appliances couldn't do, allowing familiar single-purpose devices to do more than one thing, to do them faster, and with more efficiency than before.

ARTIFICIAL INTELLIGENCE

has taken marketing courses and attended numerous seminars. For that alone she damned well ought to look embarrassed.

What I dislike about her approach is this: she isn't counseling people to live their lives with dignity. She's counseling them to manage themselves—to treat their leaking bladders as if they were investment portfolios, telling them to strategize over their strengths and to cover up their weaknesses, and she's doing it exactly the same way as the sleazoids who go around telling people how to cash in on the coming economic crash or how to reap vast profits from real estate without any investment risk.

Am I being uncharitable? Perhaps. Our incontinence entrepreneur probably has the problem herself, or one of her parents has it. She's only turning a social disability into an opportunity, taking it "out of the closet and into the spotlight" as the accompanying article says. I'm sure a share of her profits from the book will go to the nonprofit foundation—of which she happens to be the founder and international president.

I want her to answer just one question: Is everything in life an occasion for management excellence? Imagine other upcoming titles in this series: *Managing Sexual Pleasure; Managing Social Justice; Managing the Seven Deadly Sins; Managing Incest; Managing AIDS; Managing All-out Nuclear War.*

Management, when you shovel all the bullshit off the wagon,

What we don't always notice is that they get us doing things their way, and that their efficiencies are narrowing the range and variety of what we do on our own. More and more, we merely interact with the various outputs of these new technologies, particularly when something important is at stake. That's where binary syntax comes in.

The new microprocessor technologies are also freeing us from menial, routinized jobs. That's good, right? What isn't so good is that most of those who are liberated land up in even more precarious, menial jobs, or they find themselves in unemployment lines,

assumes acceptance of the world exactly the way it is, and proposes a distribution of resources and skills that are designed to achieve a narrow band of goals—usually self-interest, and other antisocial hurray-for-our-side profiteering. Most of the sneering platitudes about business ethics we've all heard are entirely correct. The Golden Rule, which had its origins in the Christian concept of agape and the categorical imperative, has been transformed by management theology as *Whoever has the gold makes the rules* or *If you have a friend who is fair and true, you'd better screw him before he screws you.*

There are things in life that shouldn't or can't be managed. Some things just happen. I keep thinking about an incident several years ago involving a man who developed an unnatural fear of being struck by lightning. His fear was so great he took the measure of getting a job working in a mine. So what happens? One day while he was descending into the mine a bolt of lightning hit the elevator shaft and zapped him. He was six thousand feet underground when his fearfully illuminated moment of epiphany arrived.

Attempts to manage human love are almost as old as love and desire themselves. Very few of these attempts have succeeded, and won't—not without degrading the constituents and diminishing and destroying the human participants.

---

soup kitchens, and mental hospitals. Soon, this liberation is going to push our governments into attempting to answer the most important question of the 1990s: *What are human beings supposed to do with themselves when their labor is no longer the backbone of the productive process?* This is almost the same question governments were challenged with in the 1960s. They didn't answer it then because they were able to bury it under a flood of surplus wealth. This time, governments aren't going to be so lucky. In the 1990s it isn't a matter of too many children growing up with too-high expectations. These people are going to

ARTIFICIAL INTELLIGENCE

Modern psychology has mounted a century-long search for the motherboard of the human wiring system. They've learned how to tamper with and manipulate some sectors of the board by exposing elements of the board's conceptual logic. But whenever it has located the erotic circuitry, a bewildering series of dilemmas is encountered.

First, almost all human erotic circuitry is hardwired well before we reach adolescence. No help there. There are no readily detectable conduits to any other part of the motherboard. Psychologists insist that these conduits exist, but their lack of practical success indicates that if the conduits are there, they're to all intents and purposes more invisible than is the plan of the motherboard itself. Similarly, interface between erotic and explored subcircuitry is asymmetrical and idiosyncratic. Finally, because erotic circuits also attach relatively stable leaders to phenomena and processes within both nature and the human universe, mapping is an exercise in logical futility.

Paradigms—the Oedipus complex comes instantly to mind—remain largely conjectural, and subject to vicious professional squabbling. Erotic circuitry can, of course, be disabled by clinicians, but only by disabling or destroying the personality and body of the carrier. And as the world becomes more technologically complex, erotic circuitry has attached itself to that new

---

be crippled and embittered veterans returning from the Front.

Keeping people in obsolete and pointless jobs is not an acceptable option—either of the humane or cost/benefit variety. The promises made in the 1960s now are either threadbare or too expensive, mainly because the surplus wealth has been depleted, both materially and conceptually. We can't all spend the rest of our lives sitting around on the beach, or in drug-induced outer space, and we can't really afford to have our children teching up for obsolete or nonexistent professions.

So far, most industrialized countries have been disenfranchis-

form of phenomenal complexity with ironic unpredictability, often with thoroughly unmanageable results.

Take Herman, for example. Herman and I grew up almost as brothers, thrown together by our mothers' friendship. Like me, Herman was the offspring of a very temporary and somewhat mysterious love affair. His mother was a refugee from the early excesses—and ecstasies—of the military side of the nuclear research industry in California. His father, about whom he knew only a little more than I know of mine, was a young, charming, and totally lunatic scientist who'd been involved in the logistical side of the attacks on Hiroshima and Nagasaki. He was working on semiclandestine plans for nuking the Soviet Union when Herman's mother found out and, out of terror and disgust, left him.

She arrived in Akron in 1947 with Herman, and moved into a house not far from my grandmother's rooming house. Not surprisingly, the two young mothers became fast friends. Herman and I followed suit.

Herman was odd even as a kid, and I loved him for it. As a boy I was shy, reserved, and physically clumsy and inept. Herman was my opposite. He was smaller than I was, with a compact body that made him resemble a seal. He was as outgoing and talkative as I was shy, but like me, he was a born schemer. We as-

---

ing those who slip outside the system frame—hiding the surplus body parts and minds under the proverbial flowerpots. In Britain and the United States—the most extreme examples—the poor are no longer even hidden. Margaret Thatcher's monetarism is aggressively showing its seamy side, and the United States, stumbling along the edge of economic and social disaster because military spending is exceeding productive investment, is promising a kinder, gentler society, while the "competitive failures" freeze to death in cardboard boxes.

ARTIFICIAL INTELLIGENCE

sumed our respective roles early on. His ebullience provided me with a protective shell, an observation bubble. He fantasized and schemed. I played the role of the straight man, keeping him in the real world and out of trouble by providing a safe and receptive repository for his craziest notions.

By high school he was a bubbling frenzy of adolescent erotic fantasies and pranks it was nearly impossible to keep track of let alone keep him straight about. There was a fixation for a very sweet girl with a withered leg, another for a Japanese-born English teacher with an authoritarian streak and a terrible temper, yet another for a girl he decided to call Princess Margaret.

I helped him keep the fixations under control, and maybe it was a good thing I did. He had some peculiar ideas about breaking the crippled girl's withered leg and then building elaborate contraptions that would carry her around while she healed, and he composed obscene and racist mash notes to the Japanese English teacher, which he insisted on passing to me during her classes. I kept him away from the crippled girl, and managed to destroy the mash notes without either of us getting caught.

The Princess Margaret episodes were more serious. Princess Margaret got her name because she bore a startling physical resemblance to the buxom British royal family princess of the same name. Just what Herman found so compelling about her I

None of those techniques are going to work much longer. We're going to have to face the problems, and soon.

One of the things I learned from working in urban planning is that a limited kind of artificial intelligence is needed to coordinate the fragile physical infrastructure of mass society. No choice there. The sheer size and complexity of our support systems demand a large degree of automatic activity. The only alternative to using computers and other forms of microprocessor technology to regulate them would involve cumbersome bureaucracy—

never did quite figure out. Maybe it was because, unwittingly, she participated in his fantasies. She affected a British accent and generally acted the Anglophile in our literature classes, reciting passages from Shelley and Shakespeare at the slightest encouragement. Worse, she strutted around like a puffed-out pigeon, and sang in the school choir so loudly and off-key that her voice would have been identifiable during a nuclear attack.

I thought the girl was a buffoon, and said so at every opportunity. But I was playing Sancho Panza to Sancho Panza, and Herman was undeterred. She became the focus of a multitude of wacky fantasies, usually centering around gowns, thrones, and tiaras. Mostly it was small stuff—he managed to land a few tiaras on her anonymously, and he collected quite a few more that I was able to talk him out of presenting to her in person.

He finally got into serious trouble when he broke into the school and spent most of one night wiring up an elaborate contraption around, in, and over her desk. He built it out of spare electric motors and Christmas tree lights, setting it up so that when she sat down on it the lights were going to blink on and off, buzzers and whistles would sound, and a record player he'd put inside the desk would play "God Save the Queen."

Princess Margaret arrived at school early, as she always did, and pompous fool that she was, accepted the throne as due

---

more mind-numbing thumb twiddling and turd polishing we just can't afford.

But narrow-focus bureaucracy created from binary syntax carries with it its own set of risks. Microprocessor-based devices and systems that perform multiple tasks quickly and efficiently are one kind of beast. Bureaucratic or economic or political systems modeled on binary syntax and aimed at achieving narrow concepts of utility are a different kind of beast altogether. If such systems are to carry the chief load of menial human support, we

ARTIFICIAL INTELLIGENCE

homage and sat down on it. The lights came on, a buzzer sounded, and then everything shorted out, nearly electrocuting her. She was unconscious for twenty minutes, and might have died if the teacher hadn't arrived to give her artificial respiration.

Herman was the obvious culprit, and I was fingered as his accomplice. We were both suspended from school, but Herman's mouth and my grandmother's influence eventually got us reinstated. We even graduated from high school a few months later.

Herman was wired up a little funny, and he knew it. He once told me a story about it that's worth repeating. In the early 1950s, his mother got married. Herman's stepfather owned an appliance repair shop, fixing toasters and record players and a lot of the other small electrical gadgets that were then flooding onto the market. Herman liked his stepfather well enough, but he liked what he did for a living more. The young boy started hanging around the shop whenever he could, tinkering with the gadgets and fiddling with the tools.

One afternoon when he was nine years old, Herman found himself alone in the back of the shop while his stepfather talked to a customer at the front counter. He stumbled against a record turntable his stepfather had left running on a chair.

Maybe it was the way the turntable vibrated when he bumped

---

have to ensure that they're really supporting human activities and not merely exercising and extending their logic mission.

Fifteen years ago in Canada, a federal agency given the singular mission of developing airports managed to build a gold-plated billion-dollar airport north of Montreal, expropriating 94,000 acres of farmland from families who'd been farming there for hundreds of years. This agency was embarked on similar programs for Toronto and Vancouver before somebody noticed that the airports weren't needed. The opponents of the agency argued

into it, or maybe it was something more deep-seated and mysterious, he couldn't say. But he had an impulse to see how it would feel if he put his penis on the rotating turntable mat. He did, and the result was his first sexual vibes, as the saying goes.

The vibrations, he said, felt just fine—so fine that he had his first orgasm a few moments later, right there in the cluttered appliance repair depot.

I didn't hear this story until we were adults, of course. I guess it was just too intimate, even for his closest friend. It wasn't until he was in his late teens that he discovered other outlets for sexual gratification, although when he told me the story he claimed he still enjoyed an occasional spin on a good turntable.

I laughed when he told me that, but somehow, I wasn't too surprised. It wasn't very often he approached anything straight on.

Take the way he got to know his wife Nola. He spotted her at a dull gathering, and he fell in love, conventionally and absolutely. So did he approach her in a conventional way? Not exactly. He sidled up and asked if she'd like to see his dead duck.

At first she glared at him, silently, bug off, bozo. He stared right back, politely but unrelenting, and repeated his question. Her suspicion turned to curiosity.

"You have a dead duck?" she said. "Here?"

---

that while the agency was spending billions of dollars so a few fat cats wouldn't have to wait for flights or walk a few hundred yards in the rain to their cars, hundreds of thousands of people were waiting for inadequate public transit, thousands more were dying in hospital corridors, and the agency was running up fabulous debts it had no ability to pay for.

The official response of this agency was that such considerations were not in its mandate, and that it was therefore "unable to evaluate competing priorities." The Montreal airport is still empty today, a monument to a lesson that we have yet to learn.

ARTIFICIAL INTELLIGENCE

"Well," he grinned, "it's not really dead. It just pretends it's dead, like. So you won't be frightened. It's really very gentle if it's treated kindly. You seem like a kind person, so I'll show it to you. But only if you really want to see."

"Well, okay, sure," Nola said, intrigued and sure it was a harmless joke of some sort. "It's a boring party. Show me your silly duck."

It was a joke all right, but not the kind she expected. Herman dropped his pants and did a handstand against the nearest wall. He wasn't wearing undershorts.

Nola broke out laughing. But she must have liked what she saw because they were married two months later, and set out to live happily ever after.

Herman had gotten an appointment in computer sciences at the university, creating computer models for an obscure federal agency, and Nola was a social worker. They bought a house, and were thinking of having children. It was around that time, one night while I was having dinner over at their place, that he told the story about his early sexual experiences with turntables.

In his spare time, Herman was fond of fixing electrical appliances, like his stepfather. When he and Nola bought the house he built a workshop in the basement, and spent his spare moments fiddling with whatever he could find, fixing some of

---

Binary logic-based devices and systems have continued to invade our social infrastructure in recent years, and binary logic has slipped free of rational control. It has come to define the goals of most of our social support systems, including our communications systems and our procedures governing social and interpersonal interaction. This is where things start to go uniquely wrong, and where historical guideposts cease to apply.

Right now the different elements of our support infrastructure continue to compete viciously with one another for access to public budgets, just as if they were private corporations fighting

them, but just as often transforming them into digitized—and nonlethal—versions of the contraption he'd nearly electrocuted Princess Margaret with while we were in high school. Deep down inside he would have liked to be an appliance repairman, but it isn't that kind of world any longer. Most appliances now are cheaper to replace than to repair.

In the midst of all this happiness and contentment I guess all the elements had fallen into place, and it was time for the hardwiring to take over. Unwittingly, I had a role to play. I wasn't about to let him off the turntable once I knew how he felt about them. Shortly after he told us the story, I gave him an old turntable I bought in a garage sale.

That started it. Later on, Nola said that when he opened up the box I'd wrapped it in, he got a funny look in his eye and took it upstairs to the bedroom.

After that he started buying turntables himself. Nola got into the spirit of things, and I stayed at it too—obsolete turntables are cheap, and Herman certainly seemed to get a jolt from them.

Before long he'd accumulated a collection. He built a rack on the dining room wall, an elaborate rig wired so he could plug in the functional models, and toggle them into the stereo system through a central patchboard.

The display became a conversation piece, much better than

---

for market shares, or entrepreneurs attempting to find their market niche with the proverbial better mousetrap. There is an urgent need, as planners used to say before they were declared superfluous, to reconcile different elements of the overall system. We need to ensure that our infrastructure is not merely creating artificial demand, and that it isn't making us less human than we rightfully should be.

Renegade physicist Edward Fredkin's ideas about digital physics offer ironic confirmation of this danger. Fredkin believes that the

ARTIFICIAL INTELLIGENCE

collecting rocks or baseball hats or stuffed animals, I suppose. The full collection—the display part of it anyway—grew to fifty-six turntables, all operable, and each with a reproduction quality distinct enough that I could pick out performance differences with my untrained ear. Herman stopped repairing other electrical appliances and spent all his time working on his turntables. He kept several dozen more of them in his workshop, and from time to time he'd take reconditioned ones upstairs and replace the—how shall I put this delicately—less desirable models in his display collection.

Given his other peculiarities, the turntable collection really didn't seem that unusual. I knew another guy once who collected ceramic frogs, and they weren't good for anything. You can't play records on a ceramic frog or a collection of stuffed giraffes.

Maybe I was being a little selfish about it all. Whatever turntables did for Herman, they provided me with a bottomless supply of gags. I did silly things like anonymously sending him spec sheets on new turntables, and when we were out together I led him past stereo shops so I could tease him. He never seemed to catch on, or if he did, he didn't let on.

"Wow! would you look at the surface on that turnmat," I'd say, pointing to one of the glittery new models in the window. "You think you could stand to look at it up close?"

---

universe operates as a computer does—digitally—and that reality is grainy rather than, as conventional physics models it, fluid and continuous. Atomic reality and its components will ultimately, he believes, be revealed as comprised of elementary bits—binary units of information—a condition of being rather than a quantity or substance.

This is not the way the human brain functions, and it is radically different from how human ingenuity makes its leaps from object to context to fabrication. Human intelligence, in its pure form, is fundamentally an analogical and contextualizing process. It re-

"Sure," Herman would answer, gazing at it with mock lust. "Great set of cobbles."

"So tell me," I asked him one night, pretending to be serious. "How is it with you? Direct drive or belt? You go both ways?"

"You get a little more speed variation with belt drive," he answered. "But the subtle vibrations direct drives give more than offset that. I go both, depending on my mood."

"Really, what's the difference between a turntable and a garden-variety vibrator."

"Well," he said, with sweet logic, "you ever try to play records on a vibrator?"

He'd been collecting turntables for a couple of years when Nola left him. It seems that the turntables took over the house in more ways than one. When I ran into her on the street shortly afterward, she told me he'd replaced her.

"Who with?" I asked, surprised. Herman had stopped fooling around the day he'd married her, and I couldn't see him taking up with someone new without me finding out.

"It wasn't a who," she said, looking away. "It was a what. And you know what it was, too."

"I do?"

"He, uh, regressed," she explained, turning to face me. There

---

lies on physical data, sure, but data processing is paratactic—meaning that it tends to be inclusive, drawing in disparate phenomena and analytical glosses and making jumps laterally by metaphor and analogy. As a reasoning process, it is wide open to intrusion. Binary logic is inherently exclusive, recognizing only the data that agree with its assumptive base and generating extensions from it. Intensive or "wild" material is simply excluded. The forms and activities of the human universe aren't binary and shouldn't be dictated by the binary models of nature or science.

The current advantage the human brain has over digital com-

ARTIFICIAL INTELLIGENCE

was an unmistakable trace of puzzled amusement in her eyes. Pain was visible, too, but there were no tears. "He went back to a sexual dependence on the turntables. So I told him to get his turntables to make his breakfast for him and iron his shirts and change the sheets."

"You walked out because of that?"

"Yes, I did."

Herman didn't want to discuss the breakup and I wasn't quite sure how to talk to him about it. What do you say to a man whose wife leaves him because he's having an affair with a bunch of turntables?

I could see he was unhappy, but he didn't seem to be willing to beg Nola to come back. Her demand, not unreasonably, was that the turntables would have to go. I thought about suggesting he rent some warehouse space and have a secret life. In fact, that was pretty much what I was going to suggest when I went over there the night he zapped himself.

The lights were on inside the house, but Herman didn't answer the door when I knocked. I waited, figuring he was otherwise engaged. As I waited, I flipped up the mailbox slot to see if I could see him. The stereo was on, and I could see the lights of the turntable control patchboard were lit up. But there was no sign of Herman, and all I could hear was the clicking of

---

puters is neural connectability. Any neuron in the brain can theoretically connect with another. As far as human brain architecture is understood, which is not very thoroughly, it appears to operate best laterally. The chief limitation, it turns out, is the slow speed at which neurological information travels through the human nervous system—276 miles per hour. By comparison, electronic impulses travel at 670 *million* miles per hour.

But if the human brain is a fully connected neural system it is one that doesn't operate anywhere near its theoretical capacities. So far, neurophysiologists can't explain just why that is so, and all

a turntable needle as it passed back and forth over the end grooves of a record. Several minutes passed and he still didn't show, so I pulled the spare key out of the planter and let myself in.

I found him in the basement. He was slumped over a lovely old Dual 1010 turntable, stark naked. It'd been one of his favorites—a classic, he'd called it. At first I thought he was dead, because there was water on the concrete floor, and the acrid odor of fried electrical circuits in the air. I guessed that the Dual 1010 had shorted out while he was on it.

I pulled the turntable cord out of the wall socket and pulled him off the turntable, dropped him to the floor, and rolled him onto his back. He wasn't breathing so I slugged his chest and gave him mouth-to-mouth for what seemed an eternity before his body convulsed and the short huffs of intake began again. I managed to carry him upstairs, dressed him, and only then called an ambulance.

When I got him to the emergency ward, I had to deal with the delicate problem of explaining to the doctors why he had severe electrical burns only on his pecker. It might have been funny if Herman wasn't in critical condition.

I didn't tell Nola the truth about what happened. I just said he'd accidentally zapped himself, and that I'd found him in time

---

indications are that parallel processing with digital microprocessors will be achieved long before the encoding of a sufficient number of human neurons enables us to do more than the rudimentary mapping of the brain that has already been done. Optimists believe the inefficiency may be due to limitations of the cortex, and point to the possibility of enhancing cortical function. Others point to the wealth of chemical inhibitors present in the brain, and are cautious about the consequences of tampering, positing that the inhibitors are there to keep us from data overload.

ARTIFICIAL INTELLIGENCE

to save his life. And for once, I said all the conventional things people say in situations like that. To be perfectly honest, I didn't tell her the truth because I was afraid we'd both start laughing.

He's recovered, sort of. The mishap left him with a partial sexual dysfunction he doesn't like to talk about, and he has an unreasoning terror of electrical and electronic devices of all kinds—tough for a married man with a job as a computer programmer. I have a suspicion that the oxygen deprivation caused a degree of subtle brain damage, too. His speediness and intellectual capriciousness seemed to be diminished after he recovered. The turntables, in case you were wondering, went straight to the Salvation Army.

About a year after it happened, he and Nola moved to California, where he went back to school for an MBA and then straight into project management. I don't know if he's troubled by incontinence because I don't hear much from him these days.

So we're trapped here—south of Cleveland where the passion for obsolete technologies almost kills my dearest friend, and north of Disney, where, I read in the same tabloid that featured our incontinence manager, a woman repeatedly ran over her husband with the family car because she believed he was being programmed by Mickey Mouse. She killed her husband, but where

Computers operate differently than the human brain, but with compensatory advantages: The biggest one is that the binary gating in computers occurs at the speed of light, which is a little more than 2,400,000 times faster than neurons travel within human nerve tissue. The chief limitation of computers is inherent in binary logic: computers operate by making rapid binary calculations, and are capable only of extremely limited analogical or contextual calculations.

That needs more explanation. A digital computer is capable of making rapid and accurate calculations on a problem with a

175

the Mouse is and what it is doing no one is sure. Last I saw of it was in a television commercial, and it was programming you and me to buy a new brand of disposable diapers.

There's no mystery here. The mysteries are all cheapened and obscured by the passion for management excellence. That's why there can be no romance at the end of this story. If you want that nice warm old-time feeling, drink four tall glasses of water before you go to sleep tonight and pee the bed. But when the chill of the disappearing world sets in, think of the Akron Design Center.

---

limited number of assumptive parameters, such as the calculation of the area of a circle based on the knowledge of its radius. The radius is one parameter, the formula for determining the area of a circle is the other. Given those, a computer will proceed to calculate the specific circle's area to an infinity of decimal points unless it has been programmed to stop at a point where its human operators become bored. The ability to continue with the calculations without loss of efficiency or attention to the problem is what typifies binary intelligence.

A human being can make the same calculations, but much less

ARTIFICIAL INTELLIGENCE

AKRON DESIGN CENTER ANTIDOTES
Science

a: The "Scientific Method" will be redefined as a religion, and scientific conferences be subjected to special TIA panels.

b: Military research and development projects will be outlawed. Persons involved in military R & D will be subjected to three-month tours of aversion therapy in which they will be required to study in detail the effects of any three wars on subject populations, and on the ecology and social infrastructure of afflicted areas.

c: Medical and other scientific research requiring vivisection of animals will be allowed to continue, with the proviso that any researcher causing the death of an animal will be required to eat it.

---

swiftly and reliably. What typifies human intelligence is that after about five decimal points, a human being will probably begin to contextualize the problem, deciding how many decimal points the problem setter really needs, or drifting off to considerations of what kind of circle it is, or what circular objects are, or to what degree they resemble similar geometric figures. This contextualizing isn't always directly efficient, but it has been indirectly very efficient across history. It's also fun—something no computer has yet experienced.

A computer will go on calculating decimal points to infinity,

CLEMATIS

Does Public Eye seem isolate and alienated to you? The guises I've taken thus far put me in culturally bombed city centers, in malls, in suburban ghettos, in airports. And I'm always alone, operating incognito, an investigator of the internal and external phenomena of the Akron Design Center, past and present.

It is true that I've stayed beyond the grasp of familiarity, that I've made no confessions of my innermost feelings, and that I've generally raised every barrier possible to literary intimacy. I do not wish you to make a sympathetic identification with me. That would be easy—and unproductive. I'd prefer you to identify the Akron Design Center in your own environment and mind.

Because I believe we are being stripped of intimate contact with our world and with one another shouldn't lead you to assume that I've made myself an atomized wanderer before the work of the Akron Design Center forces me to it.

I have a home and a wife. I even have children, a garden, and

---

unless, of course, a cutoff point has been programmed into it. Digital reality does not include the concept of absurdity. On the other hand, a computer is never lazy, and it does not make errors—and it doesn't ever betray its operating logic. It accepts whatever provisional assumptions about reality are programmed into it. A human being, by contrast, will sooner or later contextualize any provisional reality, placing it into context and scale with previously experienced situations and problems.

Admittedly it's the "sooner or later" that's the problem. It may be too soon, and it may be too late. Traditionally it has been too

ARTIFICIAL INTELLIGENCE

neighbors. My life is as normal as it can be, given the mission I'm on. To illustrate that domestic normality, let me tell you a story about my neighbors, one of them in particular: James.

James was a model citizen for the kind of digitized world we've got. He was intelligent but thoroughly conventional. He tried out everything that was easily accessible. With his short attention span, he was the perfect consumer, the sort that jumps headfirst into whatever he finds—or is put—in front of him, provided it is attractively packaged, compartmentalized, and contains no visibly dark or slippery materials.

He started off the way most bright, conventional people do — by going to a university. By the time he moved into the basement suite next door he was working on a Ph.D. in creative mathematics, spending much of his day hunched in the semidarkness of his apartment in front of a computer that seemed to be, along with a powerful stereo set, the most important components in his life-support system. The Ph.D. seemed to occupy some of his time, but that's all. He acted like a man who had a mother phoning him every night and telling him to keep working at it.

The first time I spoke with him he announced that he was a creative mathematician. I came up a little short when I tried to imagine what that might involve.

"What is it that you do in creative mathematics?" I asked,

---

soon—history is filled with lazy and precipitate assholes, and so, probably, is your workplace and your neighborhood. The examples are so many and so obvious you can select your own.

Right now our societal and political reliance on binary infrastructure is so great that we may end up contextualizing too late. As our logical systems become more complex, and as they extend themselves to the point of megalethal absurdity on assumptions that are humanely incorrect or inadequate (as with our nuclear defense systems), our ability to reprogram them—to reassert humane control—diminishes.

smart aleck that I am. "Look for creative ways of counting to ten? One-four-nine-three-six-eight-ten instead of the usual way?"

He didn't crack a smile. "No," he said, sounding as if he were reading from a cue card. "Creative mathematics is an attempt to magnify the universe by using digital formulae to penetrate or alter the conception of it."

"Interesting," I said, still not entirely illuminated. "Could you give me a for-instance?"

"No," he answered, as if refusing to explain was a perfectly normal response.

That first conversation was one of what I later came to recognize as one of his lucid moments. He didn't have a whole lot of them. Later, in another one, he told me that while he was at the university, he'd been more interested in enlarging his mind than in magnifying the universe. Freely translated, that means he'd been fairly systematically trying out whatever happened to be coming down the semilegal conduit of the consumer pike: sex, drugs, rock 'n' roll. He smoked dope in about the same volume I smoke cigarettes—I smoke a pack a day—and he dropped acid at least once a month. He wasn't very discreet about any of it, particularly not with the acid. We always knew when he'd dropped acid because the stereo got turned up about twenty decibels higher than usual, and he left his door wide open.

I've used the most dramatic example available to illustrate my point, and that might be misleading. The real problem might be that our support infrastructure is loaded with minor binary systems we have functionally lost the will to recontextualize. These systems don't do much by themselves, but together they have become almost wholly demoralizing and in some cases malevolent. Annual world spending of $900 billion on weapons of destruction while millions die of starvation and billions more live in poverty and misery is an irrefutable signal of system malfunction, but it's also too dramatic. It isn't until you're confronted by a

ARTIFICIAL INTELLIGENCE

In a way, he never seemed to be aware that anyone else was there—unless, of course, he or she intruded on his logic procedures or into its narrow range of focus. In that sense he really was digitized. He assumed everyone else lived in the same kind of on/off reality he inhabited. That's one of the things about him that fascinated me. He was utterly comfortable dropping acid in a basement suite apartment in our little section of nowhere, but he'd also have been comfortable modeling strategies for nuclear war at the RAND Corporation, or running a death camp for the Nazis, provided they showed him a good time.

Sometimes it made him a lousy neighbor. The loud music woke up my kids and bothered me and Cleo, my wife. I don't think it was because I'm getting old, either. He played the kind of lousy music any sleepy shithead on earth can get dropping by the mall and buying whatever records are being played three times an hour on the local Top 40 station. "Let's Run Away"; "Party Time"; "I Want You, Baby"; "Let's Screw", "Let's Get Stoned."

His physical androgyny and carelessness gave the impression that for him sex was probably like everything else: strictly a consumer experience. I saw him bring home partners of both sexes, but by the time he'd been there a year, there was a detectable trend toward males.

---

welfare clerk who can't help a sick or starving person because there's no appropriate program niche that you see it at the local level. And we are seeing just that all too frequently.

Just to complicate things further, there's another kind of artificial intelligence on the technological horizon. The kind of limited computers I've been talking about—they're called von Neumann computers after the man who blueprinted them thirty years ago—aren't what computer scientists are talking about when they talk about artificial intelligence. What they intend is a digitized ap-

For a while I was mildly curious about the way he related socially. But eventually—in self-defense—I decided it was like his other habits—consumerism and noise. The music I've already complained about. You could hardly escape that. The other noise was the kind he and his friends made on their own. They sat out on the small patio next to our front porch whenever the weather was decent, and yakked. They yakked mainly about fashion and accessories—which clubs were in and which were out, and which beer was the best.

I wasn't eavesdropping. When I'm not tracking the Akron Design Center, I'm a serious gardener, and I spend a lot of time outdoors digging dirt and fiddling over plants too fragile to survive in this climate without help. Sometimes I can't avoid hearing what my neighbors are saying.

Don't get the idea that I've got something against gays, either. As I said, James and his friends were model citizens. They were never violent and they never did anything seriously criminal unless you think getting bombed on restricted chemicals is a serious crime, which I don't.

Maybe that was what bothered me—they acted as if their lives were rented. Like anyone else, gays tend to be interesting people at the radicals, but when you get near the middle of the spectrum, they're every bit as dull as heterosexuals at a suburban

proximation of contextualized thinking. They're on the threshold of building computers that will be able to do this, using the electronic speed of binary processing to effect what they call parallel processing. When they succeed, and it seems inevitable now that they will, they may be able to emulate rudimentary human contextualizations at thousands of times the speed—or at hundreds of thousands of times the speed.

I don't know how that sits with you, but for me, it has mixed implications. I happen to believe that the purpose of life is to create intelligence, so at one level I'm delighted by the thought of

ARTIFICIAL INTELLIGENCE

Tupperware party or a football game. James and his friends were absolutely middle-of-the-road gay. With some of the gays I know, being gay is a signal of a serious attention to one thing or another, just like gardening. But James's homosexuality was as empty as heterosexuality—another anxiety-creating purchasable consumer identity. It was *happening* to him, not the other way around.

The most spirited discussion I ever heard come out of his place was a late-night argument over which of the "Miami Vice" television stars they'd most like to give a blow job to. That time I guess I was eavesdropping. The argument raged, sort of, for the better part of an hour, but they never did come to a decision.

What got James and me talking in the first place was the result of his drug use. I have a large clematis vine climbing up the side of my house, and James developed a phobia about it. Whenever he got particularly stoned and happened to notice me out in the garden, he'd come out to discuss it with me.

I'd be poking around with one of my plant-breeding experiments and I'd see him standing outside the door of his apartment looking as if he were having a hard time deciding which foot to move next, or maybe wondering how he'd come to be there. He had what might have been mistaken for "a scholar's air of perpetual distraction." In his case it was just drugs.

---

a new kind of contextualizing intelligence. I'm also fairly nervous about hanging around an intelligence that is thousands of times more quick-witted than mine, but which doesn't eat, doesn't get indigestion, and doesn't ever have to head off to the washroom. It won't watch sunsets and it won't goof off to play baseball on sunny Sunday afternoons. Consequently, it just won't get the subtle—or gross—kinds of physical feedback human beings get. That will no doubt make it somewhat impatient and unforgiving, rather like the privileged members of our own species.

There is the distinct possibility that the artificial intelligence

Whatever it was, it bred an absolute routine. He'd stand there for a while, perfectly still, and then I'd see him sidling along the sidewalk until he was underneath the vine. He'd stare up into it for a moment or two, and then move farther along the fence until he was close as he could get to where I was working.

He never looked me in the eye when he talked. The opposite, actually. He'd hang his head and pick at his teeth as if he were prying the words out one by one.

"You know," he'd say, "your vine is invading your house."

From there the conversation was utterly predictable. He asked the same questions each time, as if the topic were new to him. And once I figured that out, there was no point in varying my part of the script. He wasn't listening anyway.

Still, it was sort of entertaining to go through it with him. He'd drop the opening line and I'd look carefully up at where the clematis was beginning to peel the shingles off the upper portion of the wall. In several places it'd gotten into the gutters and had traveled up beneath the heavier shingles on the roof to emerge near the crown.

"Yeah, I guess maybe you're right," I'd answer.

"Why don't you stop it? It isn't good for the house."

"What for?" I'd reply. "It's just a house. And I kinda like it this way."

---

that gets created won't be at all like us, and that we may be on the verge of creating an aggressive new life-form we won't be able to compete with. This new artificial intelligence is likely to be hostile or indifferent, because it will be operating on speed—or binary—logic, not by analogy or organic logic. At very least it will be a different kind of intelligence, and it isn't going to think of us as gods, because the software needed to program this into it would use up too much memory—if not all of it.

ARTIFICIAL INTELLIGENCE

That would send him picking at his teeth even more furiously. "Well, you shouldn't let a thing like that"—he'd point to the vine—"wreck your house."

"Why not?"

"Houses are worth money. They're valuable."

"The vine is valuable too," I'd say, being just a little mischievous. "And it's alive. The house is only dead wood, nails, and some plaster."

At that, he'd grunt and take a step backward. "It looks bad," he'd say.

"Oh, I like that part," I'd answer, pretending I had the wrong kind of aesthetic sense. "It's organic. Vines are intelligent, did you know that? They're the Mensa Club of the botanical kingdom."

That would move him another two steps back. "It could take over the whole house."

"Sure," I'd say agreeably. "I saw one once that was more than sixty feet tall. Had the whole side of an apartment block completely wrapped in vines."

"What about the people who lived there?"

"What about them?" I'd say. "Listen, they thought it was just fine. The vine would come into their bedrooms at night and crawl inside the blankets and tickle them. Don't you like to be tickled?"

THE GLOBAL VILLAGE

When Marshall McLuhan coined the metaphor of the Global Village to describe the effects massive increases in the volume and speed of information flow were going to have on human societies, he misread several crucial aspects. Most of his misreadings come from the same source. McLuhan was a Christian, blinded by the optimism and belief in the essential benevolence

His eyes would bug out at that. "It did *what?*"

"It crawled into bed with them and tickled their toes. They thought it was kind of sweet, you know. Look, no clematis vine has ever been known to harm human beings. Vines just don't kill people."

"Well, you should cut that thing back anyway," he'd grumble, and then announce that he had to go somewhere in a hurry.

He and I repeated this conversation about every three weeks all one summer and fall, until the clematis stopped growing and dropped its leaves. Only then did he stop trying to get me to do something about it. (In case you're interested in getting one, the clematis was a *Montana Rubens*. They take a lot of upkeep, but they're completely harmless, and each spring you get thousands of pink blossoms that last up to a month if the weather is good.)

You can call James whatever you like—dilettante, ditzhead, drug fiend. But mostly he was the kind of person you wouldn't pay any attention to if you saw him walking down the street or met him at a party. And after you got to know him, you'd have had a hard time caring what he did with his life or what life did to him. He wasn't quite a vegetable, but he produced no blossoms to speak of either, really. His phobia about the clematis makes him sound odder than he was, and probably more interesting. I didn't think

---

of invisible authority inherent in Christian doctrine and practice. That he thought computers would save us from our own stupidity may now seem laughable. But it's typical of a man who believed that if we ourselves weren't able to control our fate, then God would. A more serious error was that he didn't foresee that Global Village culture was going to be, for practical purposes, the consumerist monoculture of Los Angeles. In his optimism he overlooked the degree to and speed with which information output sources would become centralized.

Techno-optimists continue to promise a decentralization of

anything serious would ever happen to him. But I was wrong. Boy, was I wrong.

The trouble started when his house was sold to a religious sect. I'd explain what the sect was secting on behalf of, but I was never sure. Whatever they professed to believe in, real estate, loud music, and staying up all night were the items of faith they practiced most vigorously.

If you took the collected beliefs and psychotechnologies of say, the Human Potential Movement, the Shiite Muslims, the Rajneeshee, and your local real estate board and applied them situationally, you'd have a fair description of the sect: liberty, authority, sexual self-indulgence—and you get your hand cut off if you make an investment error or offend an important person inside the sect.

When the other tenants in the house started moving out and the sect members replaced them, I didn't get too excited one way or the other, and neither did anyone else on the block. We have a tolerant neighborhood. There's a houseful of Rastafarians down the block, white guys with their hair toqued up in dreadlocks, marijuana plants in the windows, and all their women with black eyes from getting punched out. They play reggae music loud enough to wake the dead, and drive around in a bashed-up VW van painted gold and with a decal of the Lion of Ethiopia, Haile

---

output—along with a democratization of access—but the evidence indicates that while the possibility is certainly inherent in communications technology, its applications tend to be singularly centralized and one-dimensional. Where eccentric applications have occurred, they tend to have little impact, functioning chiefly as a means of institutionalizing the lunatic fringe. In the real world, it works like this: a few thousand people in specialized audiences might watch local programming—more often than not this turns out to be an irregular mélange of tourist films, corporate propaganda videos, or racist propaganda from the

Selassie, damned near life-size on the front spare tire cover. Maybe they're trying to wake him up from the dead.

Next door to the Rastas is a houseful of Vietnamese. They're fine people when they aren't running around wearing hipwaders and rubber gloves and slaughtering full-grown pigs in their kitchens. They electrocute the pigs with hot-wired lamp cords, butcher them, and then roast them over the fireplace. I have a certain fondness for victims of electrocutions, but in the spirit of cross-cultural tolerance I stuffed my feelings. I had to.

The first time they slaughtered a pig it made such a racket Cleo sent me over to find out what they were doing. They said it was a religious rite and told me to buzz off, and that freedom of worship is guaranteed under the Constitution. One of them brandished a butcher knife in my face for emphasis.

I'm not one to argue basic rights with a man holding a ten-inch blade, so I went home and phoned the Humane Society. The Vietnamese family told the same story to the Humane Society officer who came around, with exactly the same emphasis. He went away white-faced and shaking his head. Since then, the Vietnamese family has kept right on exercising its basic rights on the pigs without being molested by either their neighbors or the authorities.

*　　*　　*

Aryan Brotherhood. But millions of people see mass network's programming on a regular enough basis that their lives are scheduled by them, and hundreds of millions of people find themselves watching the Academy Awards or the Emmys—the mass media's all-star games.

Issues of quality and demographics aside, the cultural transaction that matters most is that they're all sitting immobilized in front of television sets. Television signals have the peculiar effect on the human brain of generating alpha waves, the presence of

When the sect moved in I assumed that James would move out with the rest of the people in his house. Instead, he opened his soul and his small apartment to the sect, turned his stereo up even louder, and adjusted. Probably he just smoked more dope and spent more time with the computer.

Before too long, though, his friends stopped coming around. The sect members were *real* party animals, with an emphasis on the animal part. They beat up one of his friends one night and threw him out on the street without any clothes. I had to give him an old pair of pants and a T-shirt so he could get home. Never did get them back.

And before too long James began to resemble the sect members. That was more difficult than it might sound, because he had long blond hair and a beard, and most of them were dark with sleek hair. Arabs, several of them, or East Indians. I didn't ask them which. James didn't cut his hair or beard, but he started wearing the same kind of clothes the sect members wore, and they gave him one of their ID necklaces to wear—fat beads with an enamel mandala hanging down from the middle. I used to joke to Cleo that the mandala consisted of a dollar sign and a condom superimposed on a background of chemical symbols, but the truth is that I've never taken a close look.

James was different from them in one other respect. The sect

---

which make us highly receptive but more or less incapable of critical judgment. About this side of television, McLuhan was correct. While we're watching it, television itself is both the medium and the essential content. The ostensible content of the programming is secondary or even tertiary.

Once one wades through the pluralist nonsense from television apologists, it becomes evident that only an elite is likely to gain full utility from the medium, and that this elite is going to be wealthy, powerful, and corporate. For most of us, the communi-

members, like all zealots, carried themselves with the insouciant self-certainty people have when they're utterly protected from the existential moments that assail ordinary egos. With this bunch, it wasn't what you'd call serenity. It had a distinct edge of arrogance to it, as in, we've got the system figured out, pal, and we've got the locomotives, so keep your ass off our track.

At first, James's otherworldliness fit right in. But after a week or two, it began to visibly fray, and at the loose ends was a detectable fear. Cleo speculated that he was afraid because the sect used different drugs than the hashish and LSD James preferred. The sect members were a hyperactive lot, and she figured they preferred cocaine and high-octane psychotropics.

The sect purchased the house toward the end of winter, while the clematis was bare and dormant. As spring progressed, the vine awoke. Long purple shoots began to snake their way across the house and along the telephone and power cables. Or into midair, looking for new things to wrap themselves around. James reacted predictably. His long-standing uneasiness about the clematis mated with his new anxieties about the sect, no doubt deciding that all the reaching tendrils wanted to wrap themselves around him.

James must have somehow transmitted his dislike to the sect, because it wasn't too long before they began to get aggressive about it. I knew the vine was in danger one windy night when I

---

cations impact will be mostly subliminal. The poor are becoming poor in a brand-new way, and the rich are getting richer in a new way.

Longtime trend hyena Stewart Brand describes the contrarium of information this way: "Information wants to be free because it has become so cheap to distribute, copy, and recombine—too cheap to meter. It wants to be expensive because it can be immeasurably valuable to the recipient. That tension will not go away."

Brand's personification of information isn't entirely accidental. It's typical of the way media "experts" talk about information—as

heard them out in their yard chanting "Kill the Monster! Slay the Beast!" I got out of bed and looked out the window. A group of them was at the fence in a semicircle, glaring up at the softly waving foliage. James was with them.

I got dressed and went out on the balcony, where I did my best John Wayne–type U.S. marshal impression to keep them from crossing the fence for a mass attack.

"All right, you guys," I drawled. "Calm down and can the singing."

I must have sounded more convincing than I felt because they stopped chanting. "That fucker is evil, man," one of them said. "You better chop it down before it takes over."

"Maybe," said another, "we will do it for you, eh?"

I decided to go all the way with the John Wayne act. "Well," I said, "I keep a loaded twelve-gauge shotgun in my bedroom, and that vine is on my property. I'm mighty fond of it, and I'll blow the kneecaps off the first one of you who lays a hand on it."

I owned no such weapon, but I figured a threat like that would make them think twice about crossing the fence. If they went after the vine, they might not stop there. The vine is part of the house, and I have a wife and kids living in the house.

"You wouldn't do that, man," the first one who'd spoken said in the same aggressive tone.

---

if it were a natively anarchic, partly sentient *being,* one that can act the role of Al Capp's shmoos from the old L'il Abner comic strip one moment, or John Wayne the next.

Properly considered—without heroic personifications—information is nothing more than organized data, which means that there is a logic to the way it is classified and collected, and that it has inscribed pathways and designated uses. It also means that someone has designed and executed the data processing and software.

We should all remember that this is the underlying reality of all

191

192

I noted that he moved a step back from the fence as he said it and I got caught up in the drama. Half believing I could do what I said—and completely forgetting I had nothing to do it with—I stuck to my original, nonexistent guns.

"Try me," I answered. "I place a mighty high value on the safety of that vine. It'll be in bloom in a few weeks, and you'll see why."

Appealing to the aesthetic sensibilities of a bunch of drugged-out religious fanatics was as pointless as appealing to the aesthetic sensibilities of a bunch of real estate developers. Since these guys were both, for a moment I feared I'd blown my whole act. Luckily, none of them seemed to pick up on it. I saw James sidle away and slink back to his apartment. I wondered if I should call him out and say I'd shoot his kneecaps off first, but decided not to.

"Now, break it up," I told the rest, still sounding as stern as John Wayne. "This here is a decent neighborhood. Folks are trying to get some sleep."

Without waiting to see what they'd do, I turned my back and went back inside, feeling as if I were strutting back to the marshal's office.

James knocked on the door around ten the next morning. Cleo took one look and yanked him inside. I was having coffee in the

electronic media, and we should likewise remember that the first extensive data bases were aimed at financial and political control, and that security has grown into a full-fledged information industry obsession. Much more now than a decade ago, actually. Maybe after we've thought this through, we will yap in a different tone—one not so sanguine as that of the industry's flacks—about the ingenuity and resourcefulness of those first hackers who invented the microprocessor motherboards that have allowed ordinary citizens a moderate degree of access to information and its operating technology.

THE GLOBAL VILLAGE

kitchen, reading the newspaper. She led him into the kitchen and sat him down at the table.

"Coffee?" she asked. "Would you like some coffee?"

James was so jittery he could barely speak. "No thanks," he mumbled. "A glass of water, please."

I was pissed off about the episode during the night and I went on reading the newspaper without looking up.

"I'm sorry about last night," he said. "Really sorry."

"You should be," I grunted.

"Those people," he said, "you don't know what those people are like."

"Probably not," I admitted. "I don't think I want to, either."

"No," he said, so insistent that he get my attention that he pushed my newspaper aside. "You should. You should, really. They're crazy. Dangerous crazy, like."

Cleo brought a glass of iced water. "Dangerous crazy how?" she asked.

He took a sip from the glass and shuddered. "They've got it all figured out so they can do whatever they want and no one can touch them. The police can't touch them and neither can the courts, even though they're doing all kinds of illegal stuff. They deliberately mix everything together."

"Yeah, I think I read about these guys," I said. "Real pragma-

---

Brand is right in saying that the tension between free and secured use of information isn't going to go away. He (and you and I) should pay our closest attention to how, where, and why free access is allowed, and to what effect. Another term for information is *control data*. By itself the expression invites us to be conscious of who manipulates it. It can mean "controlled data" or "data that controls."

McLuhan's Global Village metaphor is also incorrect in another key aspect. The sylvan mystique implicit in calling it a "village" promises a moderate scale of community life, one that is merely

194

tists. They set themselves up as a church so nobody can criticize them without getting sued, or accused of being a racist or a religious bigot. If someone is foolish enough to try to blow the whistle on them, a lawyer flies up from Los Angeles and hits them with a lawsuit. Then they run the sect like it was AT&T, with monthly profit and loss statements. Shit."

"You can't even criticize them if you're one of them," James said, scrunching himself down in the chair. "If you do you're subject to discipline."

"What kind of discipline?" I demanded.

"Different things. I don't really know. They beat up on one another, and there's a lot of mind-control stuff. And last week they raped one of the women and claimed that was discipline. Things like that. You should have seen it."

"I'll pass," I said.

"No," he insisted. "They're weird that way. Lots of free sex, any kind. But you have to wear rubber gloves and condoms, because the Big Man down in Southern California says that there's a sexual Armageddon coming, and he doesn't want any infection to get into the sect."

I couldn't help taking a shot at that one. "Everybody thinks Armageddon is coming," I said. "If they're right, covering ourselves in latex rubber isn't going to help."

---

contextualized and adumbrated by electronic technology. McLuhan believed—no doubt sincerely—that the smallest communities would gain a degree of access to information identical to that of the metropolises, and that this would democratize and enrich opportunities across the new civilization. Unfortunately, the von Neumann "neighborhood," the five-cell theoretical unit on which microprocessors are based, hasn't turned out to be the kind of neighborhood human beings can inhabit in an egalitarian way.

The Global Village is turning out to be eminently urban in character, not sylvan. Because it is primarily an output system, it

James shook his head, as if trying to clear it of his terror. "Do you know how rich these people are?"

"Not exactly," I said. "I just have nightmares about the lunatic fringe and the center stream of this culture becoming interchangeable. I know a lot of those born-again Jesus organizations operate the same way. It's getting hard to see the difference between the loopy fanatics and God-fearing Americans."

Cleo interrupted. "I do know one thing," she said. "You should get out of there. As soon as you can."

"Sure," he said, with a helpless smile, "I'll try to. I guess I should."

The doorbell rang. I got up, walked to the door, and opened it. It was three of the sect members, one male and two women. I'd heard the two women, Southerners, talking in the yard several times. Missionaries. One of the women ordered me to send James out.

"James will come out when and if he wants to," I said, stiffly. "Get off my fucking porch."

None of them moved. "Send him to me," the same woman said, her voice laden with threat. "If you don't I will see you as a hostile interloper and the organization will take measures accordingly."

I didn't move, either. I was almost helplessly admiring her act.

---

has imperialized its megalopolitan obsessions and its consumerist values into the hinterlands, making the entirety of North America an economic and cultural monoculture. The hinterlands have become impoverished suburbs of a limited number of megalopolitan output and profit collection centers. In North America that means New York and Los Angeles, and if Canada is lucky, Toronto.

There's astonishingly little intake or recycling of anything, least of all data. A Global Village flow diagram would look something like this:

But if I'd had a tail, it would have been between my legs, despite my brave intentions.

James shouldered past me. "Thanks for listening," he said, looking as if he'd just been condemned to the firing squad.

We didn't see him for almost two weeks. I wondered what they'd done to him, but since spring was in the air I forgot about him, figuring that if things got really difficult, he'd make a break for it as he did with everything else. We wouldn't see him go, but that'd be no great loss.

I had other things to occupy me. The buds of the clematis were swelling all over the vine. Spring was arriving. In a week, the vine would be a cloud of pink blossoms. I was spending most of my days in the garden, digging in last fall's compost and preparing the beds for planting. Most of our neighbors were busy with their own seasonal rituals, some of them planting vegetables, others planting annual flowers or pruning up perennials.

The sect seemed to have seasonal rituals, too, but theirs weren't organic. They were nocturnal. As the weather warmed, the parties went outdoors more often.

I didn't have much stomach for taking them on unless they went after Cleo or the clematis, so I tried hard to ignore them. It seemed as if they'd taken my John Wayne act to heart because

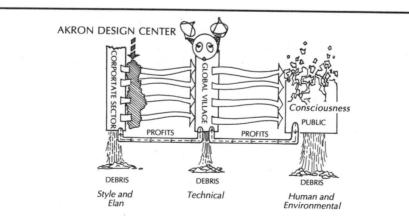

THE GLOBAL VILLAGE

there were no more chanting sessions. Maybe James's apparent fall from favor had something to do with it.

But they made it impossible to forget they were around. Most of their ritual activity was sexual, judging from the grunts and groans Cleo and I heard as we tried to sleep, and the rubber gloves littering the lawn in the morning. I'm no voyeur, so I didn't look. And anyway, the clematis was in bloom, a charge far superior to watching a bunch of real estate mystics covered with pink latex rubber get their rocks off.

Then, one soft May night in the midst of one of their performances, we heard James screaming. I'm not sure what it was they did to him that night, or were trying to do. Maybe they were gang-raping him, or something worse. It isn't something I want to dwell on.

But we couldn't help hearing his howling and screeching, and the next thing I knew I heard something scuffling against the side of our house. Serious scuffling. I jumped out of bed and dressed, and made it out onto the balcony just in time to see his head appear above the balcony roofline. There was a look of sheer terror in his face, and his eyes bugged out like saucers in the moonlight. Then he screamed and disappeared again, taking a large part of the vine with him. There was an odd sound as he landed, not so much a thump as a crunching sound.

The first thing to note about the figure is that it is hardly the depiction of a dynamic information system. It takes in raw materials, and spits out product. But the feedback loops are limited, and the system ignores its sources of materials and energy.

Eventually, one of three things is going to overtake this system: (1) the supplies of materials and energy will run out because the material and energy intake is so great; (2) the garbage it produces (and fails to recycle) will bury it; or (3) human creativity will be extinguished. We can hope that one of the first two will occur

When I peered over the edge of the balcony, the first thing I saw was the cloud of moonlit pink clematis blossoms covering the ground. Four of the male sect members were standing around in its midst, looking up at me with feral grins on their faces. On the other side of the fence, James was lying facedown on the ground in an awkward posture.

I'm no hero. I ducked inside, phoned the police, and told them I thought someone had been seriously assaulted and injured, and that there was big trouble. I gave them the address and said that they'd better send an ambulance. Then I locked all the doors of the house, got a softball bat from the basement, and stood in the darkened kitchen waiting for whoever showed up first.

The cops didn't get there a moment too soon. When the first squad car pulled up, there were seven sect members in my yard, four of them on the back porch and the other three digging and chopping away at the vine. The moment the squad car screeched to a stop outside they scattered, several of them down the alley and the others back inside their own place. I ran out and told the police officers what I thought had happened, and then I went out into the garden to see what was left of the clematis. And maybe what was left of James.

He wasn't there, and it took the cops almost fifteen minutes to find him. The sect members had dragged him inside and locked

---

before it destroys our minds, and more, that we can dismantle and retool the structure before any of the three doom scenarios becomes irreversible.

Okay. So far this is just a jeremiad. How about some practical suggestions?

I have at least one major suggestion to make. It begins with a conceptual adjustment. It isn't an easy one, because it's going to be like changing from rubber rain gear into a bathing suit during a typhoon. Initially, I admit, few will see any point in such an exercise, since the obvious thing to be doing in a typhoon is

him in a closet. From talking to the ambulance attendants later, I deduced that James had probably landed on the picket fence. They thought some vertebrae had been crushed, and he was in a coma.

The police arrested all the sect members they could catch, but two days later they were all back, and the charges had been dropped. James didn't get off so easily. The blow to his spine transformed him into a paraplegic. When the sect members dragged him into the house and shoved him into the closet, that made him a quad. That's what the doctor said at the inquiry, at any rate. He also said that if James does come out of the coma, the best he can hope for is that the government will set him up with a computerized wheelchair that lets you move around by blowing into a tube.

"It'll be a matter of what he's got inside him that'll decide how he does from there," the doctor said. "He'll never be able to lead a normal life, but if he tries hard, he can put together the pieces and make a decent try at it. It's amazing what technology can do for the differently abled nowadays."

Domestic life goes on for Cleo and me, but it's going on without the clematis. The fanatics had torn out more than half the roots, and shredded or hacked through all the main stems. The vine

---

looking for cover, just like any paranoid reptile would do. 'Fraid that won't do for us. This metaphor and crisis are about losing our fear of getting wet.

We have to make a sharp distinction between culture and economics that makes sure the actual decision-making power belongs to active culture rather than to expedient economics. To do that, we have to resist the intellectual and political Terror that is convincing us our expensive station wagons and the asphalted driveways we park them on—along with the gas barbecue on the sun deck—are worth dying for. We have to declare our solidarity

was more or less destroyed, and I decided I'd better remove what was left of it.

I thought about making a few more changes around the place as well. I could have cut down all the other vines, given up gardening, and put in an electrified seven-foot grid-mesh steel fence around the yard. I could have installed electronic burglar alarms throughout the house, with a couple of television monitors doing surveillance into the yard, front and back. I could have gone out and bought a 12-gauge shotgun to put in the bedroom closet. I could have added canisters of Mace, tear gas, a flamethrower, a rocket launcher, maybe even some tactical nuclear weapons.

But when I looked out the window into the backyard, such improvements would have made it too barren out there, even though I could have explained it by telling myself—and you—that it's the way things have to be now. Broken down into nice, sterile, isolate parcels. It makes me think of James and his creative mathematics. He'd like it that way. But so would the Akron Design Center, and I won't play their game.

So here's what I did do. I redug the sidebed where the clematis had been, and I planted three new ones—another *Montana* and two smaller *Armandi* that'll stay green all year. Then we threw a party to celebrate the plantings, to which I invited all the neigh-

---

with our neighbors and our cities and those customs and simple decencies that help us to live with and in them without exploitation and violence.

The Information Age contains the seeds for both massive transformation and reactionary insurgence. Technology able to effect the transformation of human subsistence economies—and we who live in the industrialized states *are* in the clutches of new and pervasive subsistence economies ourselves—into cultural choices that are more than consumer alternatives is already with us. Unfortunately, right now the technologies are in the clutches

bors, including the Rastas, the Vietnamese, and anyone in the sect who cared to come.

At the party someone mentioned—very loudly—that the sect was operating its commune in violation of the zoning bylaws, a revelation that everyone found deliciously funny and which we agreed—also loudly—to do nothing about.

A couple of days after that, a real estate agent showed up and planted a FOR SALE sign in front of James's old house.

---

of dull functionaries and crazed millenarians—and our institutions are in the hands of lunatics and incompetent bores. The decisive trajectory of every economic system in the world is the depletion and degradation of human and natural environments and a general reduction of organic life's variety and complexity. If we don't move to take power from the reptiles, we don't deserve to survive as a thinking species. We will be succeeded by cockroaches and amoebas.

AKRON DESIGN CENTER ANTIDOTES
Public Safety and Criminal Justice

A universal and permanent debate on the chief threats to public safety will be initiated. The debate must be open-ended, with annual referendums to determine the top ten threats to public safety, along with a listing of ten "jerk-of-the year" designates (no prize or penalty will accrue to the latter). Ten large cash awards will be provided for citizens who offer workable and/or humorous solutions to public threats.

This program should, by itself, sufficiently alter our perception of public safety so that we will recognize that the primary threats do not come from isolated and/or deranged individuals.

a: All criminal corrections and social restraint agencies will be operated by PUS draftees.

b: Seventy-five percent of police forces and police boards will be operated by PUS draftees.

c: Public stocks will be reinstituted as punishment for nonviolent criminal behavior. Citizens convicted of nonviolent antisocial acts, such as impaired or dangerous driving, fraud, theft, and white-collar crimes of a wide variety will be required to spend weekend terms in prominently displayed public stocks in order to alert the victimized communities. Sentences will be concluded by terms of service in the PUS labor pool.

ABOUT PUBLIC EYE'S PARANOIA

At a number of points in this book you might find yourself wondering if Public Eye is suffering from paranoid delusions, and if the author of this book might be similarly or even clinically afflicted. Don't think that the thought hasn't occurred to me. It has. In fact, the possibility that I might be clinically paranoid has been a compositional preoccupation. One needs to be nor-

d: Acts of physical violence against citizens serving sentences in public stocks will be severely punished, in unspecified and arbitrary ways. On the other hand, creative forms of teasing and nonviolent practical joking carried out at the expense of public stocks clientele will be encouraged by small capital-cost grants.

matively sane in order to credibly interpret a world in which all fact has been theoretically and technologically undermined. Ergo, let's look at what the literature on paranoia has to say:

Paranoia (Gr. para: "beside"; nous: "mind"). To be beside one's own mind—that is, adjacent to it.

As a clinical disorder, paranoia has a variety of figurations, almost all of which seem to be episodic rather than progressive, and tend to operate with the patient's personality relatively intact. The exception is paranoid schizophrenia (split head) in which the patient is really pretty much permanently nuts. Paranoid disor-

203

INVISIBLE MAN

Tony grew up a few blocks from where I live. I'm thankful I didn't run across him while he was growing up. It's a nice, moderately safe working-class neighborhood. At least I prefer to think so. I can't afford to move into one of those new developments with security gates and razor-wire fences hidden behind aesthetic landscaping, and I wouldn't if I could.

I wasn't around here when Tony was growing up, but if I had been, chances are I wouldn't have noticed the scrawny blond ten-year-old with bright blue eyes scouting backyards for a B and E gang of teenagers older and larger than he was. If I had, he might have blown my head off with the stolen .38 police revolver he carried in his bulky shoplifting jacket.

I missed him, but then so did the entire cultural and educational apparatus of Western civilization. I'm not kidding in the least when I say that.

---

ders are defined by the presence of delusion, usually persecutory or jealous and often systematized. The key symptom is extreme rigidity of perception, leading to irrational delusions.

Paranoids tend to be angry and frightened by the world around them, and they tend toward notions of persecution and conspiracy. Paranoids often act as if they know something that others don't. They are hypervigilant, and appear to treat everything as either significant or potentially significant, and they are always questioning motives. Information processing levels are extraordinarily high. In some respects, paranoia is a symptom of system

ABOUT PUBLIC EYE'S PARANOIA

Tony was invisible from the day he was born. And no, I'm not being mystical. The world he was born into had less magic in it than most of us can imagine. For the first part of his life it was also a world without government and bureaucracy. There's no record of his birth because he was born in the bedroom of his mother's small apartment. She didn't like hospitals, I guess, or maybe she forgot about them or didn't want to get tangled up with the authorities, even to give birth to her child.

How he survived infancy and early childhood may have involved magic. There was a lot of luck involved, and it's certainly a mystery. He has no memories of it, no mementos, and neither does anyone else. His mother was a junkie turning tricks from dusk to dawn—or trying to. When she wasn't working, she was circling the planet looking for the Man, fixing, on the nod, looking for the Man, and so forth. For her, it wasn't a very large planet. And it didn't include Tony's father. She didn't know who his father was, let alone where he might be.

Tony didn't ever make it to school. His mother didn't get around to sending him. She was busy with the Man when he reached school age, so busy that she forgot he existed for weeks at a time as he became less dependent on her. When she was capable of remembering him, her work schedule just wasn't compatible with that of a schoolchild.

---

overload, generally the result of internal psychological contradictions or (less frequently) of chemical imbalances. Paranoia is a frequent response to amphetamine and cocaine abuse, and to a lesser extent to the use of marijuana, alcohol, and psychotropic drugs.

More frequently, however, paranoia is the result of immigration, emigration, and other profound instances of environmental or physical disruption: exile from grounded consciousness.

Clinical treatment for psychotic episodes is variable, and related to the severity. Drug therapy may range from the use of mild

For him the home planet consisted of whatever slippery surfaces were presented for him to cling to or crawl under. He learned some things about it, and he didn't learn a lot of the things most kids do. He naturally came to think of his world as a normal one, because it was the only one he had.

He had a quick mind, quicker hands, and feet that were quicker again. Without those, he might have done worse—or better. A car might have run over him, one of his mother's johns might have molested him or kicked his head in. On the other hand he might have blundered into the hands of some benevolent social worker who, after a few obligatory *oh mys* would have put him on a treadmill to another authority and on his way, half-educated and half-psychotic, to a working-class suburb and a life of petty crime, legal sexual assault, and eventually to a pickup truck, color television, and chronic wife-beating.

But Tony moved so quickly he was invisible.

When he was sixteen his invisibility failed him for the first time. The police trapped him inside a house during a B and E, and because they couldn't identify him—and he refused to (or couldn't) identify himself—he was charged in adult court and sent to a holding prison to await trial.

By this time, he was slim, good-looking, and not very tall, and

---

sedatives to brain bombers like chlorpromazine. In milder cases, simple restraint and rest suffice. A third alternative is to remove or alter the causes of the paranoia.

It is this third alternative that interests Public Eye, who believes that the twentieth century is witnessing a fundamental and malevolent reorganization of human intelligence. He believes that in the latter part of the century, there is evidence to indicate that the reorganization has become covert and purposeful—that what began as a dynamic evolution has become a deliberate attempt to shape human consciousness into a passive new formulation in

ABOUT PUBLIC EYE'S PARANOIA

he had a sunny smile that had gotten him out of a lot of tricky situations with marauding social workers and his mother's associates and friends. Outside, those physical qualities helped to make him invisible. On the inside, however, they made him visible to certain elements of the inmate population in roughly the way a juicy, glistening salmon would be visible to a school of hungry sharks. And within hours of entering the institution, the sharks began to circle.

These people are called, in prison argot, mudsharks. It doesn't take much imagination to figure out what's behind the expression. Tony didn't quite know what was going on with the men wandering back and forth on the catwalk outside his cell, but he quickly sensed the danger. For several days he stayed inside, spoke only when spoken to, and watched the mudsharks glide back and forth outside his cell, whistling and grinning, almost literally clicking their jaws in anticipation of the feast.

Tony's first cellmate was a stroke of pure luck. He was a man in his thirties named Ed Baines, in there awaiting sentencing on a charge of killing a police officer. He was headed for a very long sentence, and there were rumors that whatever sentence he got, he was marked for execution, and that the only safe place in the world for him was inside a jail cell. Ed's tough reputation was deceiving. He was soft-spoken, fairly well educated, and he had a

---

which collective consciousness is greatly and artificially enlarged.

I think he's on to something. The organization of the human brain has always mirrored the pragmatic environment human beings have had to cope with, and the social configurations that have evolved as a result. In a simple world, such as existed well into the second millennium B.C. (and for much longer in some parts of the world) bicamerality—the separation of rational and holistic brain activities with minimal interaction between the two—was an adequate operating system. After that, species

distaste for mudsharks. He watched them cruise back and forth. Knowing what they had in mind for Tony, he made some practical suggestions.

"How old are you, kid?" he asked.

"Dunno," Tony answered. "Eighteen? Sixteen?"

"Well, look. This isn't a nice place. You shouldn't be here. It isn't safe for you. If you're sixteen you can go to a juvenile joint."

"How?"

"Request a transfer. Ask the bull for a transfer form."

"I can't write," Tony said. "I can't read either."

The older man looked mildly puzzled. "How come?" he asked. "You're no dummy."

"Dunno," Tony shrugged. "I just never got around to school."

"Shit, kid," said Ed. "You grow up on Mars or something? Everybody goes to school."

Tony laughed. "Yeah, well, I guess I must have grown up on Mars."

Ed tried. He called a guard and requested the appropriate forms. But because the system could kick out no information on Tony, he was presumed to be an adult: a child, in a civilized society, cannot have an unrecorded existence. That was unthinkable. The system can't accept that a child has no recorded documents. The inmate in question, it reasoned, must therefore be

---

crowding and interpenetration of social customs and environments forced the partial integration of the cerebral cortex along with a dominance of left-brain navigation. This created the Heraclitean watershed of ratiocinative self-consciousness we appear to be at the limits of today.

If we look at conditions in the industrialized mass societies, particularly during the latter part of this century, what we see isn't a river, and no one with a full deck would willingly choose to step into it. What we see is the visible or impending depletion of material resources, vastly increased populations, and the intro-

ABOUT PUBLIC EYE'S PARANOIA

adult, because adults can and often do have illegal identities. Tony was therefore declared an adult and left to fend for himself. Ed educated him on the habits of mudsharks, for what it was worth. And he armed him with one of the short homemade knives that are among the primary tools of social life in prison.

Two days later, three mudsharks cornered Tony in the prison shower. He killed one and made a serious attempt to fillet the others. That got him a second-degree murder charge, a life sentence, and a trip to a maximum security prison several thousand miles away. For seven years he became completely invisible.

Tony is twenty-three years old before he becomes visible again. Nobody really knows much about the years in between, and I, for one, don't want to know. He's full grown now—more than full grown, actually. His upper body is a mass of muscle, and nearly every muscle has a tattoo. He's been pumping iron, and he's acquired maximum security cover—which is to say, every possible location on his body has a tattoo. He's also learned a prison trade. He now inflicts the tattoos, some on his own torso, or on anyone else he happens to like.

A few battle scars have also been added, and a few body parts have been altered or deleted. His nose has been broken, the tip of

---

duction of "virtual" environments. Highly sensitive, complex, and fragile infrastructure appears to be demanding a further integration of the human brain, one that will necessitate an end to the dominance of ratiocinative individualism and an integration of automatic cortical functions with right- and left-brain capabilities. We have to become more uniquely human than we are, not less.

What we are getting, instead, is a regressive cortical dictatorship conditioned by left-brain digitizations—a dominance by the reptilian core stimulated by remote control systems. Instead of an

a finger is gone, along with his tonsils, appendix, and front teeth. What you notice about him are his eyes, which at first glance resemble small chunks of blue ice. He's added a reputation to this physical array. Among guards and inmates, he's regarded as a person you'd better leave alone unless you're willing to take it all the way. Tony is visibly ugly, in other words.

Visibility is a relative thing, in prison as elsewhere. Intimacy makes human beings visible, for instance, if only to one other person. Tony lucked out when they sent him back. The first person he saw when he got out of the holding tank was Ed Baines. The two quickly became mates.

Ed's motives are difficult to figure. He and Tony were never lovers, even though Ed arranged for him to be on the same tier, and eventually to share a cell. Ed protected him, too, as far as possible. Or needed. And somewhere along the line he slipped inside Tony's icy-eyed defenses.

Ed had become the prison's inmate librarian. That makes prisons sound better than they are, because prison bureaucracies don't have a great interest in learning or in literature. The books Ed presided over were mostly pulp novels—Westerns, military pornography, life-style novels all the way from popular romances to Stephen King. No matter. Ed convinced Tony it would be a good idea for him to be able to read and write. It was a good way to

---

enhancement of our uniquely contextualizing consciousness, we are seeing the imposition of remotely stimulated binary reflex systems that impose motivation and authority on us subliminally. This new consciousness is being imposed, when all the rationalization is cut away, in order to preserve the small and shrinking enclaves of material and social privilege—a tiny minority of selfish fuckfaces willing to sink the human species and the planet so it can wallow through another thirty years of gravy.

That's what Public Eye believes, anyway. My own view, as the

ABOUT PUBLIC EYE'S PARANOIA

kill time, he said, and the library's the quietest place in the joint.

Time was something Tony had lots of, and he'd developed a strong hunger for silence. And, having made the decision to go for something, it was not his nature to do it halfheartedly. Within a couple of months he could read at sixth-grade levels, and writing followed on the heels of reading without any great struggle. Two years after he started reading, he took the high-school equivalency exams and passed.

I met him about a year later. I'd signed a contract to teach university courses at the prison. The program I was working for was an experiment, I was told by the professor who hired me. The educational theory was that most people who commit crimes do it not because they're inherently violent, evil, or even stupid, but because they don't have the cognitive equipment that allows most of us to navigate our way in the world. My job was to teach inmates cultural and cognitive literacy, he said. He left it up to me to decide what that might be.

Well, nothing in those ideas was in conflict with my small core of liberal values, and where there was neither fit nor contradiction, my need for liberal condiments like food, shelter, and croissants supplied the linkage. In short, I needed the money. I'd never seen the inside of a prison, and I'd never been curious

---

author, isn't quite so extreme, since I have to live in the world—not merely, as Public Eye does, inside my mind. Out here it's one thing to recognize the truth of something, quite another to reflexively believe that you know it and to act on that belief. If I acted on Public Eye's approach it would lead to more or less instant institutionalization.

Still, it worried me enough that I called up a clinical psychologist I happen to know, and asked her if she would mind giving me the same diagnostic tests she gives to people who land up in the

about prisons or prisoners. But on a dull January morning I found myself in a makeshift classroom inside a maximum security prison standing in front of fifteen or twenty men. All of them were what nice folks call "hardened criminals."

Tony was in that class, and I picked him out right away. He looked as hard and mean as anyone there, a glow-in-the-dark hostility in a phosphene sea of testosterone. But there was something else there too. In his eyes was a hot curiosity that softened the cold stare.

God knows what it was he saw in me. Maybe it was the way I tripped over a chair in the first few minutes and disappeared behind the desk, or maybe it was when, trying to answer a hard question minutes later, I stuck my cigarette into my hair and flashed myself. Each time, the entire class broke up with laughter. The second time, Tony laughed longer and louder than anyone.

I didn't tell them I'd done both stunts deliberately. I'd learned that the safest way to relieve a tense situation is to make people laugh. And the safest way to make people laugh is to make oneself the object of their laughter. It was dark in that classroom that first day, and I knew that breaking down the conventional authority relations would let some light in.

As the classroom began to empty two hours later, Tony ap-

---

psych ward. I explained to her that I was writing a book that appeared to have a wide streak of paranoia in it, and that I wanted to know if it was possible to assure my readers I'm not nuts.

She said sure, and set a date for me to do the tests. There were two tests. One was the Minnesota Multiphasic Personality Inventory (MMPI), which is a 566-item true/false questionnaire subjected to computer analysis. The other test was the *Psychodiagnostik* originally developed by Hermann Rorschach in 1921, coupled with the more recently developed Exner evaluative method.

proached me. "I picked up on you," he said simply. "It's a good routine."

At first I feigned ignorance, but when I saw he didn't buy it I admitted the truth. "I needed to make what I was saying human," I said. "You guys don't need any more authority figures."

The cold blue eyes darkened perceptibly. "Explain," he demanded.

"What I'm going to be teaching is stuff that has accumulated over thousands of years—it doesn't belong to the authorities. What's good is that it doesn't belong to any one person, or rather, it belongs to anyone who wants to claim it as his own."

"Sounds like social worker shit."

I shrugged. "I'm not here to save anyone," I said, venturing onto shaky ground. "Knowledge is the only thing that can't be taken away from you. For that reason alone it's good. Outside, that's true too. I don't own these ideas, the government doesn't own them, and neither does the Corrections Service. Any idiot can get hold of a book and read it."

Tony turned his back on me. "You take too much for granted," he said quietly. "Catch you later."

A couple of classes later, Ed Baines came in after class on the pretext of borrowing some books. He told me about Tony's recently acquired reading skills. I tried to apologize but Ed waved it

---

The full text of her clinical interpretation of the test results follows, without comment or editing. Both she and I recognize that these tests have limits. The chief ones are that they're focused on determining *which* psychiatric abnormality is present in the subject, not on whether or not an abnormality exists. They're also tied to normative Western values that may have limited validity. She also had some professional concerns about protecting herself and the sanctity of the analytic methods, so it's a subjective analysis.

*   *   *

away. "You can make it up by giving him the best stuff you've got,"
he said. "And by watching your mouth."

Giving Tony books was easy enough, but keeping my mouth
shut was impossible. There were no more remarks about idiots
and illiterates, but genetics has placed my feet mentally close to
my mouth and instinct has instructed me how to use them: when
in doubt, put your feet in your own mouth. My instincts also told
me I didn't have to worry about Tony.

Both instincts were accurate. My classes stayed full, although
at least half the class regarded the course strictly as comic relief
from the grind of prison. Tony laughed with the others, but for
him it wasn't simple entertainment. He was fascinated, and it
wasn't very long before some of the defenses came down and he
began to confide in me.

The confidences were small and careful, and more often than
not I didn't recognize what they were. He was always there
before class started, silently sprawled in the chair opposite my
desk. He rarely offered conversation, preferring to listen and ask
questions. After a while, I began to ask him what I suspected
might be unsafe questions.

At first the questions were simple, like where's so-and-so
today?

"He's in the Hole," Tony would answer laconically.

The subject of this evaluation is a forty-four-year-old writer who
during the course of writing a novel became concerned that his
central character might appear merely to be suffering from
paranoid delusions. He sought the opinion of a psychologist
familiar with paranoid disorders.

During the discussion the author began to question the possibility that the character may be expressing elements of personality peculiar to himself, that is, that the author himself may be
paranoid. An unpleasant thought indeed, but not a totally foreign notion, nor one he had never considered previously. Cer-

ABOUT PUBLIC EYE'S PARANOIA

"Oh yeah? How come?"

His reply would generally be the one-word codes for offenses inmates got charged with: brew (making home-brew wine), incident (a confrontation with a guard or social development officer), hassle (a conflict with another inmate).

When he realized I didn't always know what he was talking about, he opened the codes for me, but in his own way. He never described specific incidents—that would have gone beyond the small edifice of trust established. Instead, he explained the quirks of personality and judgment that generated typical reactions. And he picked his spots. Our conversations were always timed. He sat down to talk just before class, or just before the noon or afternoon count.

Along with his impeccable sense of timing, he was a shrewd judge of character. That made sense. For a long time he'd had to know whom he was talking to and what about, just as he'd had to know exactly where the entrances and exits were and who in the room was packing a knife and who wasn't.

At first, he talked only about abstract ideas and other people. But the first time he talked about himself, he went right to the bottom line. It was just before an afternoon class. I looked up to find him staring at me. Nothing unusual in that, but what he said next was.

---

tainly the idea that many writers work out their own unresolved conflicts through their art is not a new idea. Going somewhat beyond his own personal concerns, he also felt it might be an interesting and valuable step forward to acknowledge such conflicts openly, to state unequivocally that he felt this was an absolute possibility and one that he was willing to put to the test, literally. Thus this result.

The psychologist agreed to test the author, notwithstanding that the results of the testing might be biased somewhat by the unusual circumstances of the request. Two standard psychologi-

"You know," he said, "I don't think I'm going to make it."

I was only half paying attention. "Make what?"

"Make it out of here."

"What makes you say that?" I asked carefully, not quite sure what he was talking about.

He pushed his dental plate out between his lips and stuck it in his shirt pocket. The two-inch gap made him look like a sucker-fish. My eyes bugged a little, and he smiled. "When I got sent to the Special Handling Unit I decided I was dead, emotionally. But that was okay. A dead man is invulnerable."

"Interesting logic," I offered after a respectable silence. "But a dead man is also dead. And you're more alive than most people I see."

"Well," he said, the smile going cold for a moment, "being dead was useful. It kept the sharks away. I had to pipe a few, but word got out pretty quick."

I admitted that I knew about his reputation. Beyond that I merely shifted in my chair—no comment either way. There was a long silence.

"Fuck that stuff," he continued at last. "My head's changing. It's a problem. All this intellectual shit you're peddling is interesting, but it's dangerous."

"How can it be dangerous?"

---

cal tests were administered, both commonly employed to assess mental disorders, including paranoia.

The results of the tests were rather interesting. The overall subject profile that emerged is that of a well-adjusted individual who is free of serious psychopathology in general and para-noiac tendencies in particular. There is evidence of unconventional thinking, a somewhat rebellious personality, not inconsistent with the occupation of an author, and especially one who sees himself as a critic of a society bent on self-destruction. There were tendencies toward a desire to ex-

ABOUT PUBLIC EYE'S PARANOIA

He went silent again, staring—at the middle of my chest, to be precise.

"When you've got nothing in your head there's no delay in your reaction time," he said. "Knowledge slows you down. I mean, when a guy is coming at you with a shank, you just act, dig? If you start thinking about what's happening, or what to do about it—let alone what it all means, and why violence isn't good for the health of civilization, he's going to plant that shank between your ribs."

That made sense, and I said so. "But what can you do about that? Stop thinking?"

The smile disappeared. "Naw," he answered, "don't think I can. And anyway, I don't want to die ignorant."

The system had it in for Tony. In its jargon, he had long been a serious *behavior problem*. The inmates had another more expressive term for it. They'd have said the system had a hard-on for him. What that meant is that over the years the prison system had built a book on him, learned where his buttons were and how to press them. Tony had played his side of it, too, reacting predictably and usually violently.

Now that started to change. It wasn't my influence, and it wasn't exactly that he was learning to turn his cheek. He was

---

perience life at an intense level, to seek drama, and to enjoy theatrics.

On close examination of the issue of paranoia, a very interesting finding surfaced. The second lowest of his clinical scores was the score measuring paranoia. It was so low, in fact, that it could be interpreted to suggest the presence of a well-developed suspiciousness capable of denial of paranoid personality tendencies. In contrast to high scorers on this scale, extremely low scorers are usually distinguished by cautiousness, suspiciousness, distrust, and denial, and are better able

acquiring a new sense of tactical wisdom. He'd discovered history's oldest and most stable truths about social control—that ignorance is the medium of any authority's power to control individuals, and to succeed in this, authority must cloud its operating procedures with mystery. The less a man knows about them, the more the man is a victim. And the best victims of all are those who don't believe they're victims.

Tony was right when he said that knowledge was dangerous. His discoveries were kicking him out of step with other inmates, for whom the prison system is as much glorified as it is hated. That's at the root of the inmate code of masculine solidarity: the system gets you to take a swing at it, and then it decks you. Getting hit means you're solid. Ironically, the harder you go down and the longer you stay down, the more solid you are.

The moment Tony stopped taking his swings on cue, he ceased to be predictable. And to the system he became an anomaly, and perhaps even a mystery. Here was a man it had had bagged for years, and now he'd somehow slipped the topknot and was absent.

To make matters more complicated, around that time Tony fell in love with a woman Ed knew, named Medina. She'd been a regular visitor at prison socials for several years, but why she was there in the first place I couldn't say. Friend of a friend, maybe.

---

than high scorers to judge what constitutes socially acceptable self-descriptions than are patients who exhibit overt signs of paranoia. They may, however, be perceived by others as stubborn, touchy, and difficult at times.

There was also evidence of depression indicated in the subject's Rorschach results. This leads to the speculation that the subject's clearly high information processing levels—which are common among paranoids—may be manifesting instead in depression.

If it is the author's view that the contemporary world is a place of sadness, of danger, and of isolation, it is not surprising

ABOUT PUBLIC EYE'S PARANOIA

For all I know it might have started as a visit to the zoo. Lots of women go in for that. But in Medina's case, I don't think so. You'd expect someone with her life experiences to give any man with a history of violence a wide berth. The motives of women who get involved with men who are in prison are like the reasons the men are in prison in the first place: never simple, and never the same.

Why Tony found her attractive is easier to explain. She was of medium height, although the stiletto-heeled black knee-boots she wore made her seem taller. They also made walking an adventure in balance, which made her appear as fragile as she was. She was beautiful, with olive skin and deep-set dark eyes, and together with her jet-black hair, gaunt features and a slender body made her fragility seem permanent and damaged—a kind of damage the proximity to muscled, hormone-driven men accentuated.

Like Tony, life hadn't treated Medina kindly. On her fourteenth birthday she'd been abandoned by her parents to a trio of uncles who raped and beat her for the next five years. She escaped by marrying a thirty-year-old acquaintance of the uncles, a truck driver who also beat and occasionally shared her sexually with his friends. She had two sons with this man, but immediately after the second was born, she went into hiding with

---

that to a person of any sensitivity, such a world might appear frightening and unfriendly to intelligence and emotion. It is this analyst's subjective opinion that perhaps we should be grateful that at least some of us who are sane have the sense to be afraid.

both of them. She hadn't been able to care for herself, but she was determined to care for her children. She did so with the ferocity of one who knows what neglect and abuse can do to a child.

Tony got interested in her when he realized she wasn't there to get meat-lockered. The "meat locker" is one of those half-secret prison institutions that are unofficially tolerated by modern prison administrations. It might be a washroom without surveillance, a closet, or even a table sufficiently covered by a tablecloth to afford privacy. Female visitors (sometimes hookers, but more often not) will enter the meat locker and have intercourse with one or two or a dozen sex-starved prisoners in rapid succession. While the meat locker is going on, other prisoners will crowd around the table or outside the washroom or closet to obscure the view and prevent official detection by the guards.

The guards usually know when a meat locker is operating, but so long as it isn't out in the open, they generally don't interfere. Releasing sexual tensions, the reasoning goes, helps to keep the lid on other tensions.

Tony'd never been fond of meat lockers. That wasn't his way, and it hadn't been, even in the old days. What he liked about Medina, he told me, was that she carried around with her a kind of solitariness, keeping clear of physical contact of any kind. The

---

DAVID ROURKE'S ANECDOTE

A man named David Rourke once told me an anecdote that changed the way I see almost everything about human and other intelligent life. We were inside a maximum security prison at the time, I as a forty-year-old university teacher and he as a forty-year-old inmate midway through a long sentence for a crime he didn't offer to explain and I didn't ask about. David is short, bald, and

first time he saw her he thought she was one of those nightbirds he'd heard about, but as he watched her, he said, she seemed more like a dark butterfly that might break if touched. She played with her sons, now four and five years old, or talked quietly and formally with different prisoners.

With Ed's help and counsel, he approached her—very carefully and tentatively, as one would approach a fragile, dark butterfly. He found her receptive, and for the first time in his life, more or less instantly fell in love.

In the next few months Tony came to me frequently to talk about her. Sometimes it was for advice—what kinds of toys do five-year-olds play with? was it acceptable to sign his letters with the word "love"? and what did it mean when her letters were signed the same way? Other times he came simply to sing, to have me witness the revelation that he too had gentle, loving instincts, and to marvel at her, at them, and at himself.

I did what I could to help. I met Medina several times outside prison, and spoke to her on the phone more frequently. She had questions of her own to ask: what was he really like? what did he think and feel about where he was? and finally, what did he really want?

I had an idea of what he wanted, but it wasn't something I could communicate easily to her. I did convince her that his

---

he looks at least fifty. He also has an unusually sharp sense of humor.

"When'd you start losing your hair, Dave?" I asked him one hot summer afternoon after a class.

His look told me it was an insolent question. Inmate code: never ask personal questions. But I'd asked it deliberately, and he quickly realized it. He lounged back in his chair and a sly grin relaxed the normal vigilance of his face.

"I was about twenty at the time, in for my first stretch," he said.

222

feelings were genuine and intense, and most important, non-violent. When she was convinced about that, and that he wanted what he said he wanted, she asked me to help begin the complicated process of arranging a Family Visit.

As part of a new program to help prisoners maintain contacts with family and community, the prison administration had installed two small mobile homes inside fenced yards near the prison's front gates, and were allowing married or engaged prisoners to spend unsupervised weekends with their spouses and children. To obtain this privilege, Tony and Medina became formally engaged.

I was surprised when the application was approved. Given Tony's record of violence, and the more or less open spuriousness of the engagement, the approving officers didn't have to allow it, and I didn't see any reason why they would. It would put Tony just that much closer to the outside—literally, because the family visiting facilities were close to the gate, and figuratively, because it was an approximation of the normal life he'd never known.

Ed wasn't surprised at all. "You're romanticizing the system," he said. "An administrative hard-on is like any other hard-on. It doesn't last forever. Security heads change, guards come and go. The ones who had it in for Tony are mostly gone. The new ones

---

"I was standing out in the exercise yard stinking of fresh fish. Over in one corner of the yard I saw a couple of tough-looking guys with baseball gloves playing catch, so I wandered over and watched them.

"After a while one of the guys noticed me standing there. 'Hey, kid,' he said, 'you want to play some baseball?'

"I said, sure, and the guy pointed to a shed about fifty yards off in the shade of the wall. 'The equipment's out there. You go get it and bring it back here.'

DAVID ROURKE'S ANECDOTE

don't want to fuck with him, and they see what he's doing now. They want to let him go. None of them can see what Tony *is*, so they're giving him the benefit of the doubt. These are still only human beings running this place, you know.

"Mind you," he went on, "if Tony fucks up just once, they'll be on him again like a wet blanket."

"Does he know that?"

"He knows. I tell him how it is all the time. *All* the time."

"So you figure he's going to make it out of here easy."

"Hell no. Anything can happen in a place like this. There are situations that come up where he'll have to choose between screwing up on the system's terms or fucking up on the terms of the guys around here. The kid is walking a tightrope."

The Friday before the visit, Tony was riding on air. I kidded him about it—carefully—but I kidded him. And I smuggled in a couple of red roses I found growing next to an abandoned house when I went out for lunch. Tony hadn't asked for them. To have done so would have contravened the contraband ruling, and he was careful not to jeopardize his friends that way. Before he left for the afternoon count, I tossed him the cigarette pack I'd stuffed them into, ice chips and all.

"You'll need these," I said. "Good luck."

"I was a pretty good ballplayer in those days, so I figured, well, great, if I show my stuff I can be one of the guys. So I walked out to the shed and went inside."

David broke out into a full grin at this point, and it looked as if he'd finished his story.

I didn't get it. "What's that got to do with losing your hair?" I asked.

"Well," he answered, looking slightly disappointed that I hadn't gotten the punch line without him having to deliver it in

224

On Monday morning he was still on air, but at an even higher altitude.

"It must have gone okay," I ventured.

"It was amazing," he said, leaning back and putting both running-shoed feet on the desk between us. He flipped open a cigarette pack, tossed me one, and lit his own. "Truly amazing."

"I'm glad," I said, and didn't ask for details. I didn't even tell him to get his feet off the desk. But later in the morning I got a message from the guardhouse that there was a call for me from the outside. When the noon count came up, I hustled upstairs to find out what it was about. It was a message from Medina, asking if I could call her back as soon as possible.

I dialed her number from inside the prison, ignoring the rumors that all the inside phones were tapped.

"You've got to talk to Tony," she said, after we'd gotten through the pleasantries. I could tell from her voice that she was troubled.

"About what? Is something wrong?"

"Well not really. I mean, I don't think so. It's just . . . that there was one thing. It was strange."

I could tell that she was nearly as embarrassed at talking about it as she was troubled by what it was. But after some coaxing, she blurted it out.

---

person, "you ought to know the answer. When I came out, I was bald."

Now it's your turn to ask two dumb but separate questions: *What happened to David Rourke inside the shed, and why did that story change the way you see the world?*

The first is the easy one. David wouldn't admit it directly, but his fellow inmates followed him inside the shed and gang-raped him. Years passed during the few minutes he was in there, and when he emerged, he was a much older man. You and I can understand what happened and why he told it that way rather

"It's just that, well, something happened when we, uh, made love, like."

"Something usually happens when people make love," I answered, unable even in that circumstance to repress the smart aleck in me. "What upset you?"

"Well, he kept *slapping* me."

"He *what?*"

She repeated it. At or near the climax of each lovemaking session he began to slap and punch her—in the ribs, and on the side of her face and head.

I told her it didn't sound like Tony, and she agreed. "He's always so gentle," she said, her voice breaking a little. "So tender. And then that. It was like he didn't want to do it, but he did it anyway. . . ."

"I'll talk to him," I offered. "And I'll find out what's going on."

I said I'd phone her that evening and hung up. If the phones were tapped, Tony would be on his way to the Hole by the time I got back.

He was in the classroom. I pulled him into the library bookstacks for some privacy.

"I had a call from Medina," I said.

The grin he'd been sporting widened. "Yeah? What'd she say?"

---

easily, but you should recognize that this simple anecdote contains such a wealth of ironic contextualizations that the most sophisticated artificial intelligence machine in the world would blow its circuits on them.

Answering the second question is going to take some doing. First of all, I have to amend my initial statement. It wasn't only *the story* David Rourke told me that changed the way I see the world. It was also David, and some others I met in jail. What we were trying to teach them changed me, and so did the way they responded to it.

225

"She said the weekend was fine. Except for one thing."

The grin faded slightly. "What's that?"

What the hell, I thought. Nothing like being candid and having a short life. "She said that while you were making love you kept slugging her."

"Yeah, so? What else?"

"What do you mean, *what else?* You're not supposed to slug the person you're making love to."

He seemed surprised. "You're not?"

"No, you're not."

His surprise turned to mixed pleasure and relief. "Oh, wow!" he said. "That's great."

It took a few minutes to get the story out, and a few more to get it straight in both our minds.

The weekend had been his first heterosexual experience. He'd only had one other "serious" relationship, several years before, with another inmate. His lover, as it happened, was a masochist who liked to have Tony punch and slap him while they were making love. The harder the better. With no other data to work from, Tony'd assumed that slugging your partner was a normal and, well, *required* practice.

"I figured it was the right thing to do," he said. "I mean, cats bite one another, and stuff."

David Rourke was—and if he's still alive he probably is—an interesting man. He was intelligent, self-ironic to a fault, and he had the best sense of comic timing I've ever encountered. It's a gift that has probably saved his life nearly as often as it has gotten him into trouble.

He's also a convicted felon with an extensive criminal record, and he might cut your face off if you turn it for him the wrong way. I never challenged him on the last part, so I can't say for sure.

When I started working in jail I carried in the old saw, "There

"Well, human beings don't," I said. "Or at least most of us don't. You don't have to. And Medina doesn't want you to."

"You explain it to her," he said. "Tell her I would never have hit her if I thought I didn't have to. I mean, I didn't whack her as hard as I figured I was supposed to. If you can, try to make it sound like I'm not a total goof."

It didn't happen very often, but that day I left the prison giggling. The gate guards searched my bag with a special, frowning enthusiasm. I told them I was smuggling an inmate out in pieces, but they didn't believe me. They didn't laugh at that, either. In a way, I was telling the truth.

For a year after that, Tony and Medina's life together settled into a strange parody of normality. They continued to have bimonthly weekends in the family visiting units, and there were the weekly visits in the common room with all the other inmates, and one or two socials in the prison gymnasium. And maybe more important than any of those, there was a stream of letters.

I saw nothing of the visits, but I did see some of the letters. It wasn't so much that Tony was taking me into his confidence as using me as his technical adviser and editor. At first they were just mushy love letters, but after a month or two he began writing stories for the kids, and love poems for Medina.

---

but for fortune go you and I" as a badge of personal and professional conviction. Within a few weeks I dropped it, because I recognized that the old homily just wasn't true. But I hung on to the appearance of it as a more or less deliberate measure of pedagogical innocence—until the day David told me that story.

There's a specific difference between you and me and most of those who commit serious crimes, and while fortune and environment have something to do with it, it doesn't alter the fact that the difference is fundamental.

He said the letters were the real backbone of the relationship. At first I didn't see what he meant, but as the months passed I began to appreciate the immense difficulty of conducting a relationship from inside a prison. And I began to see the subtlety of what he was trying to accomplish with Medina, and to appreciate him even more.

For him it was new territory, one that he entered with few skills and no experience. But slowly, painstakingly, he began to acquire skills. At first the stories were crude and simple-minded, and the poems were worse. But they got better, mainly because they had to. He was learning that Medina was a profoundly damaged human being, one he would have to heal as well as love. The odds of succeeding weren't in his favor, and he knew it. But instead of whining about it, he began to create and re-create himself in an image of maleness that would dispel Medina's fatalistic reserve—and thus allow her to re-create herself in a context that wasn't boundaried by fear. From the letters of hers he showed me, it was easy to see that she believed that all civilized behavior from any man was a veneer that circumstance and nature could and inevitably would peel away, exposing the violence and sexual selfishness that, in her mind, were the basic ingredients of male being.

Tony didn't try to argue himself as an exception. Probably he

---

If, for instance, you and I are walking down some street discussing who the best baseball player in the American League is, we are probably going to disagree. I have very strong and unconventional opinions on the subject. Same goes if I were walking around the prison yard discussing a similar question with an inmate. But at this point different scenarios are likely to occur.

You and I don't have to think twice about why we don't resolve our difference of opinion by burying axes in one another's skulls. For most prison inmates, that is often the first—and only—recourse. That's usually why they're there.

DAVID ROURKE'S ANECDOTE

had his own fears that she was right, given the overwhelming evidence of his own experience. Instead, he created an alternative and parallel universe that he tried to draw Medina into. He also began to live in it himself, and to face its consequences.

He was having serious trouble with some of his old friends. One of those who didn't like the changes was a big meatwagon who was in most of the same classes he was. His name was Herb Harbage, aka Harbage the garbage. He was a biker, about six-four and nearly as wide. All of it was muscle too. He lifted weights three or four hours a day, and was doing the same work inside as he'd done outside—being an enforcer for whoever would buy him dope and women.

Harbage looked as if he were all muscle, but he was more than that. He had some brains, and he had a very strange sense of humor. Despite knowing that his MO was tying people's feet to accelerator pedals and sending them off cliffs, I kind of liked him. There were worse people around.

Part of the trouble was that Harbage knew Medina—from where or what I never did discover. He didn't like her. Maybe it was seeing Tony change so much, or maybe it was, as Tony explained it, jailhouse politics. Whatever it was, he began to tease Tony in front of other people, which is something you don't do inside a prison unless you're suicidal or you already have your

---

You and I are different because we're carrying around embedded cognitive structures that inform us that violence is an ineffective, wasteful, and stupid method of resolving conflict. Those embedded structures also provide us with alternative modes. We might resort to rigid but quietist prohibitions, we might employ the rules of formal discourse, we might use laughter or a wide variety of sublimating strategies—all without acknowledging that we're using them or even recognizing their existence.

Those cognitive structures we carry to avoid violence are, in their complex totality, what culture might usefully be redefined

229

victim by the short-hairs. It wasn't something that anyone would
have risked with Tony a year or two before.

"Going out for another weekend in the boneyard with the
Black Widow?" he jeered at Tony one Friday afternoon before a
family visit.

"So fucking what, Garbage-head?" Tony snapped back. "You
jealous?"

Harbage laughed. "Sure," he said. "I've got a crush on you. You
know that. Don't want you sullied by a hockey stick with hair
on it."

"Go tie a barbell to your foreskin and do a couple hundred jerk
lifts," Tony countered. "You'll forget all about me."

Just before the count that same day, Ed wandered in from the
library and asked me to keep an eye on Harbage, that there was
some "bad shit" brewing. I tried to get him to tell me what it was,
but he wouldn't, or couldn't. "Just try to keep him off Tony's
tail," he said.

I didn't see what I could do, but I didn't say that. Harbage
tolerated me around the school area, but that was all. I wasn't
around the rest of the time, and if anything happened it wasn't
going to happen in class.

During the next few weeks I stepped in front of a couple of
barbs aimed at Tony. Harbage started fish-eyeing me, which

as. Most prison inmates have them in extremely rudimentary or
fragmented formulations. Many don't have them at all.

I can see only three exceptions to this. Psychopaths are one.
Nothing you can do about psychopaths, because they're alone in
a logical universe—sort of like a computer—and always will be.
The other exception is political criminals. Our prisons used to be
full of them, Soviet prisons *are* full of them, and so are prisons in
the Third World. Political criminals are guilty chiefly of holding
ideas about social justice and social practice that are different

DAVID ROURKE'S ANECDOTE

wasn't a pleasant experience. Finally, Tony told me to leave it alone. "I can handle him," he said. "You stick to what you're good at."

None of it seemed all that serious to me, but I was wrong.

For several weeks, as the prison "social" approached, Tony grew visibly apprehensive. Things weren't going well with Medina, for one thing. They were arguing during the weekend visits, and she'd stopped responding to his daily letters.

"She's depressed," he told me. "Talking about how she's ruined, and that I'm too good for her, and she doesn't deserve me. She even threatened to top herself. And," his brow furrowed at the thought, "she and Harbage have been writing letters."

"Harbage?" I asked, surprised. "He has trouble writing his own name."

Tony ignored my attempt at wit. "Well, I have a theory about all this," he said. "I think she's scared of the possibility of having me around all the time. Probably figures I'm faking it, and that I'll turn out to be the same kind of rat's asshole she's used to. Can't really blame her for that."

"Maybe she's just afraid she'll lose you once you get out and find out what she's really like. So maybe she's covering her bets. It's probably a little of both—she doesn't trust men and she doesn't like herself. The point is that you're not a monster," I

---

from those of the political authorities that govern them. They're cultural and political antagonists.

Most prison inmates in the West today don't have any ideas about social justice at all. They operate on the basis of extremely limited concepts of self-interest and ego gratification. They may sound like simple psychopaths, but they're not. They're uneasy about the way they see things, which the crazies never are. They're there because they've never been enculturated. They lack information, and they lack the cognitive tools you

said, trying to sound wise. "You know that."

"Yeah, I know who I am," he answered. "But it's what she thinks I am that matters, and what she thinks she is. It'll work out. One way or another."

As an outsider, I wasn't obliged to go to prison functions, and didn't go to many. But this time I did. I told myself it was for Tony and Medina.

I knew something unpleasant was brewing. I could smell the fumes around the school all during the week before it was to take place. Harbage was grinning constantly. Tony seemed dry and tense, and nearly everyone was giving him a wide berth.

Ed wandered in from the library several times to make sure I was coming. The third time he did it, I asked him point-blank what was going down.

He was evasive. "Nobody's in any danger, if that's what you're worried about. But you might see jailhouse politics at their best. Or their worst."

"Can't you stop whatever's going to happen?" I asked.

"Maybe," he said. "Maybe not. People gotta do what's in them to do. If they don't see what's going on and do the right thing at the right time, they're always going to be in one jail or other."

He wouldn't elaborate.

* * *

and I take for granted. In a very real sense, they're culturally illiterate.

The third exception is a real head-breaker. In contemporary culture a small minority of lawbreakers—usually wearing expensive white shirts with clean collars—wind up in prison because they're *perfectly* enculturated. They've acted out exactly what our consumerist/business-focused culture taught them to do. They're there because they were too uncritically enthusiastic, usually. If they were a little smarter, they'd probably be corporate captains.

DAVID ROURKE'S ANECDOTE

The Saturday on which the social was to be held arrived. Tony had been right. It did work out. And Ed had been right, too. I saw jailhouse politics at their worst. Or at least I saw the aftermath.

I ran into Medina at the gate when I was going in. She nodded at me, but that was all. The boys weren't with her, and she was dressed to the nines—the usual stiletto boots, a black dress with dual white zippers up the sides, and more makeup than I'd ever seen her wear. It made her large dark eyes seem even larger than usual, but the overall effect was out of kilter. The butterfly Tony had been writing letters to had been replaced by a black widow. I tried to catch her eye as she was going through security, but she wouldn't meet my gaze. She seemed nervous and determined. Oh-oh, I thought.

The guards let her through without a fuss, but they stopped me and searched me thoroughly. Someone inside, they finally admitted, had kited them with the information that I was going to be packing in drugs. I explained to them as patiently as I could that if I were going to pack, it sure as hell wouldn't be on the day of a social.

Being that candid was a mistake. Some guards are reasonable. Others, well, aren't. I had one of each on my case. The unreasonable one didn't like me anyway, and wanted to shine his

---

Back to David Rourke in a minute, but first I'll complete the redefinition of culture. Most of the time when the word "culture" comes up, what is meant is "serious" or "high" culture—genre literature, philosophy, classical or experimental music, theater and nonrepresentational visual art. The term has become synonymous in most people's minds with pissing through a straw.

Social anthropology has saddled professionals and academics with another definition of culture that is so loose that it's solipsistic. As Umberto Eco has pointed out, "even defecatory positions are part of a community's material culture."

flashlight up my ass just for the entertainment value. He reasoned that if I knew about packing and when to do it, then I must be packing. It took forty-five minutes for the reasonable one to convince him to put his flashlight away, finally telling him that if his logic was as sound as he thought it was, he'd better stick the flashlight up his own keester as well.

When I finally made it to the gymnasium, I looked around for Tony and Medina. Tony was there, in a corner talking heatedly with Ed. Medina was nowhere to be seen.

I strolled over to talk to them, but Ed spotted me coming and waved me away. He and Tony kept on talking intently, with Ed pushing Tony repeatedly back into the corner.

I scanned the room again. It was relatively full, mostly with adults—families clustered together, and one or two small children dashing in and out of the clusters, chasing one another. A few couples were dancing to the loud rock music, most of them cheek-to-cheek, ignoring the music's fast beat. At the far end was a line of tables, most of them covered with trays of bread, fruit, cheese, and cheap cold cuts. On one of them stood several ten-gallon cans of Kool-Aid, and on the table beside it was a big coffee urn.

The biggest crowd was in front of the washroom, mostly green-clothed inmates talking quietly. I looked around for the social

---

My redefining of the term would have culture restricted to those cognitive structures and social institutions that affectively instruct us with alternatives to violence as a means of resolving conflict and violence. Period.

Such a redefinition creates an interesting gloss to work with. First, it leaves "high" culture within the boundary, giving renewed value to historical record and the history of ideas while deflating the value of—and the interest in—expressive formalism.

Second, and equally interesting, it effectively places contemporary mass media and economics outside the context of affec-

DAVID ROURKE'S ANECDOTE

development officers, conspicuous in their checkered polyesters and ID tags. They'd all be carrying security buttons, and there'd be an invisible cordon of open space around them.

My room scan clicked back to the crowd near the washroom. It wasn't *mostly* inmates. It was *all* inmates. While I was discovering this, the crowd parted and I saw Medina coming out of the washroom door with Harbage right behind her. One of the inmates took her arm and tried to steer her back inside, but Harbage interceded. As the inmate let her go, she reached down and tugged at one of the white zippers at the side of her dress. Damn, I thought. Damn.

I glanced around at Tony. He and Ed had stopped talking, and were watching. Ed had his hand on Tony's shoulder.

Across the room Medina and Harbage were standing just beyond the crowd. They didn't appear to be saying anything. Medina was staring at the floor, and Harbage was talking to someone behind him. Then Medina gave him a quick embrace and strode precariously across the gymnasium to the security door, where she signaled to the guard in the bubble that she wanted out.

Tony didn't move, and neither did Harbage. The security door opened, and she slipped out and was gone. I walked to where Tony was, wondering what to say. What was there to say?

---

tive culture, pending the deposit of a performance bond. For the mass media, and television in particular, simple violence is an operational fetish. On balance, few alternatives to violence are offered as a means of resolving conflict, and violence is the chief selective criterion in mounting news and dramatic programming.

Likewise, the core values of capitalism see social and economic conflict and limited violence as their natural interactive medium. Indeed, the recent outburst of enthusiasm for those values seems designed to create a whole new generation of pro-

235

236

Ed greeted me formally, as if nothing were amiss, even shaking my hand. "Nice you could make it," he said. "We heard you had some trouble at the gate."

Gratefully, I related my confrontation with the guards, teasing it out as elaborately as I could. Tony listened with a frozen smile on his face. When I'd run the story out well past its logical ending, the three of us lapsed into a painful silence. Finally, I couldn't stand it. "How you doing, sport?" I said to Tony, putting my hand on his shoulder.

"I'm okay," he said. "This wasn't exactly a surprise, you know." He shrugged my hand away.

"I didn't know," I replied. "But . . ."

I trailed off into another awkward silence that Tony broke. "Look," he shrugged. "I got some things to weed through. Think I'll head back to my drum. Catch you on Monday, okay?"

"Sure thing," I called out to him as he walked away. "Stay cool."

He didn't answer. Ed grimaced, and then strolled off toward the food tables. Two social development officers followed Tony to the door and were watching him depart into the inner courtyard. One of them was chuckling; the other was glancing back and forth from Tony to Harbage. They'd seen the whole thing, and were no doubt relieved no one had been killed.

---

fessionally deculturated sociopathic entrepreneurs. Have a more critical look at the mission of the current plethora of glitter propaganda and antisocial self-improvement books (*In Search of Excellence* instantly comes to mind), along with the get-rich-quick seminars and secular religious cults that offer business-oriented mind-fuck techniques like neurolinguistic programming.

Third, my redefinition of culture reveals prisons as one of our civilization's key cultural institutions. By itself, that is a damning commentary. Contemporary prisons are educational facilities,

DAVID ROURKE'S ANECDOTE

I left a few minutes later, without any idea what would happen in the next two days, or if I would see Tony on Monday—or ever again. What I did know for sure was that Ed's "do the right thing at the right time" was sure as hell going to be put to the test.

Tony wasn't there on Monday, and neither was Harbage. I checked around and found out that neither was in the Hole, and that both were alive. As soon as I could I walked over to the library to talk to Ed.

"Tony's staying in his drum for a while," he said noncommittally. "Harbage is in his, too, but not for the same reasons."

"Okay," I said. "That's great. Now, just what the hell is going on? What's going to happen?"

"Nothing is going to happen," he answered. "Not a goddamn thing. Not if I can help it."

Nothing did either. The following Monday Tony was back in class. He was quiet, but cheerful enough, and he didn't want to talk much.

On Wednesday, he was abruptly transferred to a medium security unit. Two months after that he went on to a minimum security unit. Cascading through the system, as they say, but at breakneck speed. After warehousing him for a decade, the system was pushing him out like an unwanted chick from the nest.

---

with very few positive elements to relieve the twenty-four-hour-a-day training in cultural damnation inmates receive.

The small and experimental program I worked in took a self-selecting sample of inmates and taught them straight liberal arts—history, literature, and some social sciences. Operating off a philosophical framework pirated from the work of Piaget, Kohlberg, and Jurgen Habermas on human moral and cognitive development, we treated inmates not as criminals in need of punishment or therapeutic rehabilitation, but as students in need

237

I didn't see him for six months. After all, I was still in maximum security. But I heard from him regularly, and in volume.

It was an odd kind of correspondence. The first thing he wanted was information. Technical information, on the subject of motorcycles. I went down to a motorcycle shop where I knew one of the mechanics and photocopied a hundred pages of tech sheets and reviews of new machines. When more specific questions came—"Why are Harley-Davidsons so popular with bikers? Which is the best Japanese machine available?"—I put Tony directly on to my mechanic friend, who luckily was happy to answer his questions in copious detail.

Stories began to arrive—kids' stories, but this time not, as before, about dragons and knights-errant, but about motorcycles, the Open Road, and freedom. There were letters to Medina as well. They were romantic, but like the stories, they weren't the same as the old ones I'd seen. There was no mention of the breakup, no recriminations. Like the kids' stories they were filled with allusions to motorcycles and to the pleasures of being free and on the road—the closest he got to the old Tony were occasional descriptions of wildflowers seen along the road. The paraphernalia of longing and separation was still there, and so were the assurances that not all men are violent.

---

of historical data, ideas, models, and contexts, and the cognitive tools to evaluate and manipulate them.

After several years of this, prison statisticians discovered that our students were leaving prison and not coming back with the usual stunning regularity of "normal" inmates. Between two-thirds and three-quarters of inmates who commit felonies come back to jail after being released. For a while only about 15 percent of our students were coming back in, and the recidivism rate, once it settled, has remained substantially lower than "normal." I won't relate the ugly details of how nervous corrections

DAVID ROURKE'S ANECDOTE

The most curious thing about it all was that Tony didn't want either the stories or the letters back. I corrected them and edited them, and at his request, gave them to Ed. Neither of them offered any explanation for this strange procedure, and I assumed that I was witnessing some sort of bizarre jailhouse ritual—Tony proving to himself and to Ed that he could beat Harbage at his own game. It didn't quite add up, but I was discreet. Maybe, I thought, this was an archive of some sort, or an act of sympathetic magic.

Meanwhile, it was helping Tony to work his way out of major emotional upheaval, blunting a private loss that could easily have sunk him. And it was quietly and surely propelling him toward the street. The social development officers had doubtlessly reported the near incident at the social to their superiors, and the fact that Tony had not reacted with characteristic violence was almost certainly noted as an indication of his readiness for parole.

Even swift release from prison is a gradual and bureaucratized process, and for Tony, it was fraught with uncertainties. He'd had the family visits, but he hadn't been on a city street without manacles for almost thirteen years.

On his twenty-ninth birthday, I took him out for his first UTA—code for "unescorted temporary absence"—a day outside

---

professionals subverted much of our program's energies, or why. Suffice it to say that it has been vulgarized in much the same way all successful experiments are. The system wants to control, and that's been as far as their understanding has penetrated.

That brings me back to the guys down in maximum security, and to David Rourke and his lost hair. Like a lot of men I met in jail, David was very bright. His problem was that he'd never known where he was, and he'd had only a limited and paranoid view of who was running things—usually overweight authoritarians with crew cuts, polyester pants, and a worldview

prison by himself. He had to be escorted, but at least I wasn't a guard.

He'd prepared himself in a number of ways, and one part of it at least had been excruciatingly painful. He'd removed the two-inch swastika from the back of his hand, and the FUCK YOU from the front of his fingers. To do it he'd used a cut-and-burn combination of a soldering iron and battery acid. The tattoos weren't completely obliterated. They'd merely been made illegible. Now he looked like a man with conspicuous tattoo scars on his hands. It was better, but just barely, than swastikas and FUCK YOU.

He had a long list of things he wanted to see and do, on that UTA. Most were predictable enough. He wanted to drive around and see how people lived, and he wanted to walk around and see how people who didn't know who and what he was would react to him.

I picked him up at nine in the morning at the prison gate, and we drove slowly into the city. Except for the tattoo scars and the excitement in his eyes, he looked pretty much like a truck driver on his day off. As we neared the city he popped a surprise on me. He wanted to go to a graveyard first, and he wanted fifteen minutes alone.

I found a cemetery, a small one on a rolling slope, obscured from the road. As I pulled the car over and stopped he leaped out

---

strikingly similar to his own. The only successful cognitive tool he'd ever had was his sense of humor.

He knew nothing about Western civilization, and once he discovered it was there, he took to it like the proverbial duck to water. He liked its previously mysterious cognitive technologies best of all. He was instantly interested in, yet bewildered by, metaphors, which have become, in the last century, a specialist's tool to generate the specialized morphological sets that drive our vast propaganda and product advertising apparatuses. David's

DAVID ROURKE'S ANECDOTE

and disappeared over the brow of the slope without a word. I sat in the car wondering how I'd explain myself to the parole official who'd okayed the UTA. But when the fifteen minutes were up, he reappeared.

"What was that all about?" I asked as he popped back into the car and closed the door.

He closed his eyes and leaned back against the headrest. "I wanted to see if I was right about all this," he said quietly. "A few years back, that was my only other choice. I could go on living, or I could let go and die."

"Some choice," I muttered.

"The only one I had," he said. "I chose right, too. The dead are trapped in there forever. No pain, but they're in for the duration. Too long . . ."

"Let's get out of here," I said.

By midafternoon, I was totally exhausted by the sheer intensity of the intake, and I knew how Prospero must have felt with Miranda. Tony was seeing everything for the first time, and by association, so was I.

There'd been only one somber moment after the graveyard. We were sitting in the lobby of the city's oldest and grandest hotel, drinking coffee and watching the mostly elderly clientele come and go, when Tony began to fuss.

---

bewilderment derived from the fact that metaphor, despite its universality, is a complicated cognitive tool to operate. Metaphors require both specific and generalized information, and they require the skill to make half-tangible connections, along with the confidence to stay with them.

In a moment of casual mischievousness, I once told him that metaphor could give him back his hair, and that he would be able to return to that equipment shed and come out with a full head once again. Until that moment he'd been engaged in a program

"These people," he said. "They look so comfortable here. They act like they've been doing this all their lives, and that they'll go on doing it for the rest of their lives."

"Yeah," I agreed. "Homers, they're called."

"They make me feel invisible," he whispered unhappily. "It's like I don't exist."

"You *don't* exist," I agreed. "Not that way. But the way they live isn't all that great. Most of them live like blind people. They only recognize what's familiar, and nothing else registers. Because they don't bother to imagine the way other people have to live, they don't know what's really valuable, and they can't—or don't—protect what they have. It's pleasant for them, but there's no particular virtue involved."

"I'll never get to be a homer," he said.

"Nope. And you shouldn't waste time trying. I don't feel at home here, you know. Very few people in this world are not, in one way or another, living in exile. So whenever I get around these kinds of people I pretend I'm an anthropologist who's just arrived from Mars, and I try to figure out what the interesting-looking homers are trying to accomplish. It gives me a working identity. And it keeps me from getting too self-conscious, like you're doing."

Tony brightened as I pointed to an elderly couple at a window

---

aimed at making everyone in the entire world as bald as he'd been made. He laughed at what I said, but I really don't know if it changed his program.

He was still working on his own unique application of metaphor when I lost track of him. He'd told me any number of deliciously funny stories in the meantime, most of them about hair. The last time I talked to him he showed me a story he was writing about a man who forgets he's wearing a toupee and jumps into a swimming pool to impress a prospective girlfriend. When the toupee comes off and floats insistently atop the pool's surface,

DAVID ROURKE'S ANECDOTE

table playing cribbage. "So what are they doing?" he asked.

"On the surface, they're killing time—one foot in the lobby, and the other foot in the grave. That's okay. But maybe what they're doing is waiting for the arrival of some bird they know nests in the trees outside. Suppose they're bird-watchers. And that when they go home they have a houseful of exotic birds. Maybe they're working out the language of birds while they're pretending to play crib. If you look at them the right way, they even act like birds.

"It's a real life, but it isn't yours. You've got real things too. There are advantages to being invisible—no one can see you, and you can see everybody. You're going to be like this for the rest of your life. You may as well get into it."

"I've already sort of figured that out, with Medina."

"Speaking of her," I said. "What's going on with her, anyway? What was all that stuff with the letters and stories going out to Ed?"

Tony turned to watch the bird couple, as if looking for reassurance. "I made a deal with Harbage," he said.

"What kind of deal?"

"You know. I didn't want her getting smashed up again. And the boys." He cleared his throat and poked at his coffee with a spoon. "Harbage is a yahoo, but he's basically not too bad.

---

the prospective girlfriend reveals her own disguises. The story's protagonist is merely bald. His girlfriend is a male. Haw, haw.

By the time I lost track of David he was out of maximum security, trickling down through the corrections system on his way to the street, wearing the wide grin he was born with, and carrying, for the first time, what I hoped was the beginnings of a coherent culture in his head.

Now I can return to what he and his story taught me and how it changed the way I see the world: First, obviously, the story taught me not to go into equipment sheds without being wary about

He's had the hots for her for years. So Ed negotiated a deal between us."

I repeated my question: "What kind of deal?"

"Those stories you corrected, and the letters. They were for Harbage. He recopied them, and sent them to Medina. I figured that, uh, if she couldn't accept one exception to the brute rule, a second one might force her to. Harbage knew all about what I was doing with her because I told him, or Ed did. I tried to explain to him where she'd been and what she needed. He used it to get her away from me, saying he could do better. She fell for it, sort of."

"Sort of," I echoed. "Don't you think she dumped you because you were getting close to the street?"

"Oh, yeah. And Harbage has got more time left, so he was safer. I figured all that out. Anyway, he hooked her, but once he had her he was smart enough to figure out he was in over his head."

"So you helped him? I would have thought you'd have wanted to kill him."

"That's what he thought, too, at first, the asshole. But I knew why he did it, and I knew why she did what she did, and after it was done I figured there was no point in taking revenge. For one thing, it would have proved she was right about all men, and it would have proved the system was right about me."

---

what and who is inside and who will be entering behind me. Second, by example he taught me that human beings are mortally attracted to equipment sheds, and that this attraction isn't suppressible and shouldn't be. I was already convinced that any and everything is potentially funny, so that doesn't count.

But most important, he taught me that human beings make up a world with whatever materials are presented to them. A government—or any kind of authority—restricts or manipulates those materials at its peril. David, and others, also taught me that in a nonsubsistence civilization, depriving citizens of access to

DAVID ROURKE'S ANECDOTE

"She isn't right."

"No . . . but there was something else involved, that's taken me awhile to come to terms with."

"What's that?"

"Well, when I saw her coming out of that washroom, I had this moment where I could see everything I'd ever done perfectly clear. So I was standing there watching her walk across the floor, and I was thinking that if I know something, I have to act on it, or I was going to be a dead man all my life, no matter what else I tried to do afterward. And I want to be alive, to go on thinking and seeing new things. So I let it go, and I let her go with it. I made the deal with Harbage, or rather, I let Ed negotiate the deal. Maybe it'll work out for her with Harbage. Who knows?"

Tony is out on the streets now. I haven't seen him for nearly a year. Last time I talked to him he said he was taking some technical courses—something to do with radio and television copywriting. He's also living with a young woman, a photographer, he said.

I suspect the two of them have a curious kind of symbiosis going for them, with Tony discovering how things are done, and her watching him and photographing what he's able to make

---

information and conceptual tools is a perfect recipe for individual and social violence. Finally, he taught me to trust my culture—as I've redefined it—without extending that trust to its forms of authority, however subtle and seductive they become.

visible to her. If she has any talent, the photographs should be remarkable.

I find it immensely comforting. In a world where the Reptile Machine or the Akron Design Center is always watching and manipulating, bending our minds to its new authority, there is also Tony, who is everything those things are not, watching the same world, and making what's invisible visible, and vice versa.

THE AUTHOR'S CRITICISM
OF THE NARRATOR

There are two major unresolved issues in the narration of this book: (1) Public Eye hasn't pinned down the Akron Design Center. As a matter of fact, as the episodes go on, he appears to forget about it, wandering off in search of novel folk lodged in irate and asymmetrical relationships to accepted authority and custom. (2)

A PARABLE AND SOME
FINAL ANALYSIS

Adam is having a bad day.

Why? The fruits he is given to eat are unspotted and perfect in their jackets of chemical wax, the vegetables and nuts freshly washed and free of decay. The shelves of paradise are full, the aisles well-lit, safe, and sparkling clean and polished. Has not God in his high-tech labs nuked out any life-form that might disfigure or spoil the lovely products? Does not Adam's Dacron bodysuit and head cover protect him from the searing ultraviolets? Do not the implants in his nostrils keep from him the miasma of recycled air, sterilants, and improperly consumed hydrocarbons?

Yes, things are uniformly *positive* in Adam's world. Yet as he strolls through this paradise of standard commodities in the fluorescent brilliance of perpetual noon, a disquieting notion

---

Public Eye's identity and genealogy remain muddled. This lack of resolution bothers me, and I'm going to assume it bothers some of you. Ergo, I've subjected my capricious narrator to a brief interview to see if I can clean up these loose ends.

BF: You've presented us with the "idea" that there is a malevolent agency at work in the world, but it remains only an idea and a threat. Nowhere in your narrative is there a direct confrontation with it or its agents, and at the end we have seen no more of its substance than we had after, say, the first fifty pages. How come?

248

begins to nibble at the small core of his conceptual circuitry God has not yet disabled. As the notion grows, the nibbling becomes a gnawing, and soon the notion infects each and every cell of his body, whispering a satanic Truth: he, Adam, who has been made perfect, who has been freed from every hunger, can take no pleasure from perfection. He is hungry.

As this Truth alters itself in order to be articulated, synapses jangle unsteadily and anarchically across the length and breadth of Adam's brain. A family of questions is engendered in the sterility God's perfection has replicated there: *What are flavor and texture? What is satisfaction? What is delight?*

Adam shudders involuntarily. How will he now obey God's prime directive that he have a nice day?

As if in answer, a still more deadly question is born: *What is a nice day?*

For certain, Adam has almost as little appetite for these questions as he has for the commodities that surround and comfort and sedate him. No wonder. Paradise can exist only if there is an absence of fundamental questions, an environment of absolute logical predictability.

But as the ideas grow and proliferate, they begin to whisper to him. He imagines the delights and the pains and the sensory textures and flavors known by those who have gone before him,

---

PE: You're being a pedant about this. The Akron Design Center is a mutant offspring of a general marriage of authority and electronic communications apparatuses. What do you think this is? Science fiction? I haven't staged a dramatic confrontation with the Akron Design Center because if I did, the figures I would present would settle as a set of physical images readers would find easy to reject because their experience is different. And anyway, the key to the Akron Design Center is that it refuses to settle either in the confrontational frame of discourse or in the fantastical frame of fiction.

THE AUTHOR'S CRITICISM OF THE NARRATOR

and he learns, against the will of God, the language of the dead. He hears the promises made by the dead to the yet unborn. And he sees, as in a vision, the cold murder of God's absolute order.

Now, God does not like to be asked fundamental questions. His technology systems have been carefully designed to suppress, destroy, and remove fundamental questions. While he was devising the systems, God discovered fundamental questions do not exist either in nature or in logic. They are the work of Satan. Nature buries all questions with productivity, and logic closes itself against inconsistency and inefficiency—fundamental questions cannot exist in logic. Fundamental questions arise from the interaction of general principles with inefficient and anarchic specifics—Satan's realm. Accordingly, God created a Master Plan and a Design Center to carry it out.

In his plan God set down that the discomforts and inefficiencies of things and processes that are local and particular must be replaced by more profitable generics—standard commodities, standardized images, standard procedures. Private imagination must be suppressed, lest the serpent of curiosity creep in. Serpents must be declared environmentally superfluous, along with their environments.

In fact, everything that might disturb the peace and order of paradise must be exterminated. The reptiles and raptors and

---

Think of it this way: An electrical storm leaves certain sensible traceries after it has passed—everything seems clearer, as if it has been illuminated by the extraordinary expenditure of pure energies. There is the faint scent of ozone in the air, one or two visibly blackened objects where lightning has struck (this doesn't always happen, and it is the least of the actual effects) and an uneasiness—or an exhilaration—at the breakdown of meteorological stability.

As a detective, one must begin with tangible clues. I've traced the Akron Design Center from the contact points I managed to

razorback hogs must be swept away with the other biological confusions that harbored them, save for a few specimens required for museums or for experimental science. Even the wilderness that once surrounded paradise will be clear-cut.

Adam's capacity to ask and answer questions will be supplanted by an erotic desire to consume. But this Eros will have no Psyche to torment it, and no history to inform. Even death, its old twin, will have no role here. It is therefore the perfect, contentless medium, the answer to every desire, God made efficient at last.

And so God reasserted control over the world and thrust Satan into the neural wilderness.

In case you're wondering, there is an Eve in this paradise, but her curiosity has been stifled. Just now she is at an aerobics class, doing body maintenance, and from there she will go to a women's studies class, then to t'ai chi, and finally to her allergist, who will advise her, as always, to maintain body integrity through a dust-free postorganic bubble environment, obviating contact with any lurking self-motile substance.

But in spite of God's will and his glorious tech-aided order, Adam is asking fundamental questions. He wanders hither and thither in a state of spiritual distress. Eventually, seeking an answer to

---

discover, to the dissolution of its tangible effects. And there *is* a pattern. At the dissolution points, I've discovered particularities, illuminated ones. These particularities are the resistant elements that combat the Akron Design Center's growth and control.
BF: Is that all you could come up with?
PE: That's all. There ain't no miracles. Just us and the things we create and do—consciously or inadvertently.
BF: Or ignorantly.
PE: Right.
BF: On another issue, can you give us more information about

THE AUTHOR'S CRITICISM OF THE NARRATOR

his painful questions, and recalling dimly that she has had a different way of seeing things, he seeks out Eve right in the middle of her aerobics routine, and demands answers from her. But Eve, who listens to his questions and sees the misery it brings to him, says onto him, "Get out of my private space, Satan."

So Adam leaves her to her self-improvement classes and her body maintenance routines and wanders through the spotless aisles of paradise . . . and to make a long story short, he eventually finds himself in the presence of God.

Adam asks God his fundamental questions, which by this time have proliferated and mutated and become an interminable whispering that infuses everything. And to both Adam and to God the whispering is many things, the babbling of streams on a summer's day, the cries and whimpers of the disappeared and the superfluous of the earth, the shouts and roars of the cheated multitude of things.

And God, out of irritation or fear—or from his delight in efficiency, silence, and the hum of air-conditioning motors—exterminates Adam and all his kin.

This, despite the tongue-in-cheek parody and except for the twist at the end, is the millennium according to the Akron

---

who you are? You begin by revealing that you're Rainer Maria Rilke's grandson, and then, as your narrative progresses—or digresses—you call that into doubt in a number of instances. What was your grandmother's relationship with Zip? Was he her secret benefactor? Was *he* your grandfather? And what about Herman Kahn? Where does he fit in? Was he possibly your father, or was he the father of your friend Herman? Were you and Herman half brothers?

PE: Those are interesting speculations, I'm sure, but I'm not going to confirm any of them. What I will confirm is that I'm a product of

Design Center. And since this parable, and this book, are neither
religious tracts nor visionary science fiction, I would like you,
reader, to return to irritable critical consciousness wherein you
will recall that the millennium isn't yet here, and that there is
still time to prevent this general retreat to absolute authority.

Think about it. Despite the smooth surfaces, the consumerist
paradise is the renovation of a very old universe. The pre-Fall
Adam was the perfect consumer of Jehovah's inscrutable digital
authority. Or at least he was until he demanded to know the
mortal secrets of good and evil, which, translated into practical
terms, means the knowledge of context.

The Akron Design Center means to restore Jehovah's shattered order. It is intent on returning us to ignorance and innocence, and surrounding us with infrastructure that we can't
escape from.

It leaves a couple of key questions hanging, of course: Just
exactly what is it the dead whisper? What do the powers I appear
to claim for that whispering derive from?

According to my mother, who learned it from my grandmother,
who in turn probably learned it from my grandfather, the dead
whisper about local knowledge—things seen, touched, *live
things, things lived and conscient of us,* to use his terms.

Local knowledge is knowing the inherent if arbitrary and

---

certain events that transpired in February 1922, and that this
narrative is most definitely an offspring of a letter Rilke wrote in
November 1925. Beyond that I respectfully decline comment on
the grounds that to do so would be a formal diminution of the
miracle—and the comedy—of human consciousness. Examine
the history, read the letters, and decide for yourself. The boundaries of this narrative mustn't end with me.

THE AUTHOR'S CRITICISM OF THE NARRATOR

temporary cohesions of what surrounds us. It includes the physical environments we inhabit, from the hydrological systems in which bloodsuckers live and breed, to the star systems we glimpse through the smog on clear nights. But it also includes politics, be it civic, neighborhood, family, sexual—the whole constellation of biological and earned kinships that are falling apart under the onslaught of the Akron Design Center.

Of course, unless and until you deliberately assign value to these things, they're no more real than the whisperings of the dead. And unless you integrate their claims with those neurotic and willful phantoms our world glorifies and suppresses at the same time, the dead don't whisper at all.

God, I can hear you grumbling, what a lot of convoluted nonsense this all is. Okay, let me up the ante. There are immediate threats you and I must deal with. They come at us—and for us—every hour of the day, preinscribed, insinuating, habilitating. The Akron Design Center is going to come for us all, sooner or later. Inevitably. Individually or collectively.

Here in the preconstruction days of the millennium, the designers of the Akron Design Center have found ways to redesign our sense of self and our consciousness of the world around us without our knowing they have done it. After they have gone, the dead cease to whisper, and our thoughts are no longer our own,

---

KOMOS

A Komos can't be faked, not even in the old kind of genre literature. A Komos demands a public ceremony, and the sanction of a coherent community. We don't have any of those. They're over there, in that equipment shed.

But from inside the shed I can hear the dark faerie choir of manufactured deception and misperception grow louder and

our questions are atomized, replaced by prefabricated answers. It is no longer possible to be knowledgeable and private and innocent.

Oh, we're still alive, still comparatively wealthy and autonomous, still *citizens*. But the political state we exist in isn't the one we were born into, and its boundaries are dissolving. Why? Because the Akron Design Center can manipulate and adjust our consciousness of that state. And it does. Look around you.

It is a Thursday afternoon in early November as I write this. Memory day. Outside my window, a bitter wind is shredding the last few leaves, and in my world there are no roses on the table, and no brown dog trotting across a field. Such things have disappeared—roses are commercial sex-aids now, or a hobbyist's means of self-expression. Even dogs have become security devices or adjuncts to our personalities.

What an irony this all is. I am writing a progress report about a world that no longer cares if it is progressing in any direction and is too busy surfing the commodity waves to consider whether it is regressing—a world on the critical path of the Akron Design Center.

Surviving without becoming one's own branch of the police, or refusing to abandon the disorderly neural stations of the mind to any single-minded authority are day-to-day psychophysical strug-

---

more ominous, an acoustic gabble from the subterranean corridors of consciousness that threatens to engulf the sounds and shapes of our human and humane attempts to converse, to love, to remain distinct, individual, and nonviolent. Can you hear it?

The ritual avoidance of violence is the highest, and perhaps the only absolute value comedy serves. Hence, in a world where absolute violence has become an omnipresent and invisible threat, comedy must assume a more important role model than tragedy, one that is infinitely more important than is generally recognized. It is also a strategic key to the now-arrested growth of

KOMOS

gles now. As an investigator, accumulating enough clarity and will to allow *anything* to happen without undue manipulation is one part of the job. The other part is the existential insistence on seeing human reality as a social continuum and not a system— although it is becoming apparent that the rest of the universe *is* merely a system.

Remember that most of the universe is dead. There are no scented blossoms of any kind out there, no warm spring breezes, no babies crying in the night. In deep space, no one goes to sleep in the arms of his or her lover.

Who's saying this anyway? Is this Public Eye trying to tell his stories and lay down his evidential tracks? Or is this the author on his soapbox, calling for an all-out but boring invasion of fiction by ideas?

Imagine the moment when my grandfather awoke from a dream-filled sleep to find the soft lips of my youthful grandmother grazing the fine wrinkles of his forehead in the moonlight. Did the faithful brown dog stir in its hovel at that moment, did the petals of a fading rose drift down to the oak tabletop on which, the next morning, my grandfather began to write his last great poems?

Imagine the moment, two decades later, when my mother turned the key to unlock the door of the room in the now-torn-

---

humane institutions and perhaps to our survival itself. We can't afford to let ourselves be "measured" by either humourless binary logic or by nature. Only human beings can adequately measure other human beings, since we are now the caretakers and not the servants of nature, at least on planetary terms. And we must regain control over our culture and the technologies that are supposed to be acting in our service.

For me to arbitrarily declare a Komos would be to indulge in wishful thinking. As individuals and as a species we are suspended in a contrarium, poised by the violence of media before

down Akron Hotel, and allowed my father to enter first, with his unknown past and his future of which I am among the few known shards?

At the moment of consummation and conception, did any of them shudder, sensing the terrible future into which they had launched me?

I don't know the answers to any of those questions, and it's pointless to speculate on them further. I'm not sure who I am, and, more important to us all, I don't know where the Akron Design Center is at this moment or what appearance it has. If you think you've got everything figured out, don't, as the corrosive mists drift around you, be too complacent. Other, closer figures are taking shape, diaphanous and subtle, drawing you into a world of ephemeral entertainments.

Who or what will the final figures be, and who or what will be their creator?

---

either a mass funeral—not at all funny—or the promise of the sacred wedding feast a Komos is supposed to enact. Are we going to make our dim, stumbling way to the most violent of imaginable ceremonies, or will we find new pathways to the Komos, and the catharsis of folly by folly?